CORPSE TALK
QUEENS & KINGS
AND OTHER ROYAL ROTTERS

For Rowan and Mhari.

CorpseTalk: Queens & Kings and Other Royal Rotters
is a
DAVID FICKLING BOOK

First published in Great Britain in 2018 by
David Fickling Books,
31 Beaumont Street,
Oxford, OX1 2NP

Text and Illustrations © Adam & Lisa Murphy, 2018

Design and adaptation by Paul Duffield

With special thanks to
Tom Fickling, Anthony Hinton and Joe Brady.

978-1-78845-032-4
1 3 5 7 9 10 8 6 4 2

Papers used by David Fickling Books
are from well-managed forests and other
responsible sources.

DAVID FICKLING BOOKS Reg. No. 8340307

A CIP catalogue record for this book is available
from the British Library.

Printed and bound in Great Britain
by Sterling.

CORPSE TALK

Queens & Kings

AND OTHER ROYAL ROTTERS

BY ADAM AND LISA MURPHY

CONTENTS

64 RICHARD THE LIONHEART
ENGLISH KING 1157 – 1199

MOCTEZUMA II **70**
AZTEC EMPEROR 1466 – 1520

76 HENRY VIII
ENGLISH KING 1491 – 1547

HENRY VIII'S WIVES **82**
ENGLISH QUEENS
1480s – 1500s

92 CHARLES II
BRITISH KING 1630 – 1685

MARIE ANTOINETTE **100**
FRENCH QUEEN 1755 – 1793

106 CATHERINE THE GREAT
RUSSIAN EMPRESS 1729 – 1796

SHAKA ZULU **112**
ZULU KING 1787 – 1828

118 QUEEN VICTORIA
BRITISH QUEEN 1819 – 1901

SO, FIRST OFF, IT'S A **LESSON** IN BEING A **LEGEND**, NILE-STYLE. HIS BUDDIES (AND BY BUDDIES, I MEAN **GROVELLING VASSALS**) CALLED HIM "SON OF THE GOD RA, WHOSE JUSTICE IS POWERFUL, THE STRONG BULL, PROTECTOR OF EGYPT AND SMASHER OF FOREIGNERS"...

BUT **YOU** CAN CALL HIM...

RAMESSES THE GREAT!

RAMESSES II

PHARAOH OF EGYPT

C. 1303 BCE - 1213 BCE

RAMESSES, YOU MAY BE THE FIRST DUDE EVER TO CALL HIMSELF "THE GREAT", **WAY** BEFORE ALEXANDER, ALFRED, GREGORY, CATHERINE **OR** GATSBY. THAT'S PRETTY BALLSY.

PFF – **COPYCATS!** BUT THEN SINCE I AM, WITHOUT DOUBT, THE **GREATEST DUDE** TO EVER HAVE LIVED, I'D SAY IT'S ONLY APPROPRIATE.

SINCE I CAN SEE YOU'RE SPEECHLESS AT MY **AWESOMITUDE**, WHY DON'T I JUST GIVE YOU A FEW INTERVIEW **POINTERS**...

FOR EXAMPLE, YOU SHOULD CERTAINLY ASK ABOUT MY AMAZING VICTORIES AGAINST EGYPT'S ANCIENT ENEMIES, THE **HITTITES**.

OOH, I **HATE** THOSE GUYS! POXY HALF-BAKED ANCIENT EMPIRE WANNABES, COMING OVER HERE, STEALING **MY** CITIES...

WELL, THEY SOON FOUND OUT THEY'D MESSED WITH THE **WRONG PHARAOH!**

BOOYAH!

OH YES, YOU TANGLE WITH THE RAM-MAN, YOU GONNA **FEEL THE PAIN!**

BUT THE RAM COULD ALSO SHOW **MERCY**...

DID YOU KNOW I SIGNED THE WORLD'S **VERY FIRST PEACE TREATY,** WITH THOSE SAME SLACK-JAWED HITTITE BOZOS...

DIDN'T **HAVE** TO DO THAT... I'M JUST SUCH A NICE GUY.

THEN PERHAPS YOUR READERS WOULD WANT TO HEAR ABOUT MY AWESOME MONUMENTS.

LIKE I BUILT BASICALLY THE BIGGEST STATUE **EVER. OH YEAH!** YOU LIKE THAT?

AND WHEN I SAY **I** BUILT IT, I MEAN OF COURSE MY ARMY OF SLAVES BUILT IT.

HOLD ON, THERE'S MORE. DON'T FORGET TO ASK ABOUT HOW MANY TIMES I WAS MADE A **GOD.**

IT WAS LIKE **20** TIMES OR SOMETHING COS I LIVED SO LONG, AND JUST KEPT ON DOING SO MUCH AWESOME STUFF.

PLUS, I HAD LOADS OF WIVES, LIKE **200** OF THEM, WHICH HAS **GOT** TO BE A RECORD OR SOMETHING.

NO BABY, YOU'RE **TOTALLY** MY FAVOURITE!

YESSIRREE. A PRETTY **BAD-ASS** GUY ALL ROUND, AS I'M SURE YOU'LL AGREE.

...

ARE YOU **QUITE** FINISHED?

WELL, NO, BUT YOU GO AHEAD...

ALL RIGHT, FIRST OFF, THAT "GREAT VICTORY" AGAINST THE HITTITES...

ISN'T THAT THE BATTLE WHERE YOU RAN AWAY...?

CRASHED INTO YOUR **OWN** MEN...?

AND ENDED UP RETREATING HAVING FAILED TO RECAPTURE **ANYTHING?**

FINE. WE'LL CALL IT A **DRAW.**

HOW'D YOU KNOW ABOUT THAT!? I TOLD EVERYONE IT WAS A TOTAL BEAT-DOWN!

I MEAN, I...

ARCHAEOLOGY, MY FRIEND. THE ARCHAEOLOGY **NEVER LIES**...

ER...

HM.

WHICH IS MORE THAN CAN BE SAID FOR **YOU**! YOU MAINTAINED YOUR "SUPER-PHARAOH" FACADE THROUGH A SLEAZY **SPIN** CAMPAIGN OF **POLITICAL PROPAGANDA!**

AND YOU DIDN'T STOP THERE! NOT CONTENT WITH HUNDREDS OF YOUR **OWN** STATUES AND MONUMENTS...

CELEBRATING RAMESSES' AMAZING VICTORY!

RAM'S PLACE.

RAMESSES BUILT THIS.

RAMESSES, RAMESSES, RAMESSES AND RAMESSES.

YOU WENT AROUND PUTTING YOUR NAME ON ALL THE **OTHER** PHARAOHS' STUFF AS WELL!

BUILT BY KING TUT.

REPAIRED BY RAMESSES THE AMAZING!

YOU KNOW THERE'S A **WORD** FOR SOMEONE WHO TAKES CREDIT FOR OTHER PEOPLE'S WORK...

AN **IDIOT**. IF HE GETS **CAUGHT**, THAT IS...

ANYWAY, DON'T **JUDGE** ME, **MAN**! YOU CAN'T EVEN **COMPREHEND**!

I WAS BUILDING AN **ETERNAL EMPIRE**, ONE THAT WILL LAST TILL **THE END OF TIME**...

UH, YEAH. I'VE GOT SOME BAD NEWS ABOUT THAT TOO...

N**OOOOOO**!

BUT AT LEAST ONE THING IS TRUE. YOU **DID** LIVE AMAZINGLY **LONG**, MORE THAN **3 TIMES** THE AVERAGE LIFESPAN OF THE TIME...

MY STATUE...

PERHAPS THAT CAN BE YOUR NEW TAGLINE — "RAMESSES: HE MAY BE A CHEAT AND A LIAR, BUT HE'S ALSO **REALLY OLD**..."

I WOULD **SO TOTALLY** HAVE HAD YOU KILLED...

PHARAOH **RAMESSES II** IS ONE OF THE MOST REMARKABLE **MUMMIES** OF ALL TIME. WE THOUGHT THIS WAS A PERFECT CHANCE TO GET THE **INSIDE STORY** ON...

HOW TO MAKE A MUMMY

AS YOU ARE NO DOUBT AWARE, YOUR **SOUL** DISSOLVES AFTER YOU DIE IF IT DOESN'T HAVE A PROPER **HOME.**

AND SO, FOR THE MOST IMPORTANT AND BRILLIANT SOUL (I.E. MINE), NO EXPENSE WAS SPARED TO PRESERVE ITS HOME, MY BODY.

THAT WAY I COULD **LIVE FOREVER!**

MWA HA HA!

STEP 1: PREPARATION

AS SOON AS I DIED, I WAS SHAVED, WASHED AND DISINFECTED WITH PALM WINE.

ALL THIS WAS DONE IN **TENTS** BESIDE THE RIVER NILE, SO THE BREEZE WOULD WAFT AWAY ANY... NIFFY ROYAL ODOURS.

STEP 2: EXTRACTION

THE **INTERNAL ORGANS** WERE ALWAYS THE FIRST THING TO **DECOMPOSE,** SO THEY HAD TO BE REMOVED ASAP.

IMPORTANT ORGANS LIKE THE **STOMACH, LUNGS, LIVER** AND **INTESTINES** WERE TAKEN OUT THROUGH A SMALL SLIT IN MY SIDE AND PRESERVED IN JARS.

IN CASE I, Y'KNOW, NEEDED THEM.

WE EGYPTIANS BELIEVED THE **BRAIN** WAS JUST SO MUCH USELESS MUSH, SO IT WAS PICKED OUT THROUGH THE NOSE WITH A HOOK AND BINNED.

BUT THE **REAL** ORGAN OF THOUGHT AND FEELING, THE **HEART,** WAS LEFT IN.

LIGHTER THAN FEATHER = VIRTUOUS HEART.

GO TO **FIELD OF REEDS,** A BLISSFUL AFTERLIFE.

AFTER ALL, I NEEDED IT TO GIVE TO **ANUBIS,** THE JACKAL-HEADED **GOD OF THE DEAD,** FOR WEIGHING.

HEAVIER THAN FEATHER = WICKED HEART.

GET EATEN BY **AMMUT,** A LION-CROCODILE-HIPPO MONSTER.

FEATHER OF TRUTH

STEP 3: DESICCATION

THE **KEY** TO KEEPING A MUMMY FROM DECOMPOSING IS TO COMPLETELY DRY IT OUT.

THIS WAS DONE BY COVERING ME FROM HEAD-TO-TOE WITH A SUPER-DRYING NATURAL SALT CALLED **NATRON**, THAT SUCKED ALL THE MOISTURE OUT.

I WAS BURIED IN THE STUFF F **70** DAYS, DURING WHICH TIME ARMED GUARDS HAD TO KEEP WATCH AROUND THE CLOCK TO KEEP AWAY DESERT SCAVENGERS ENTICED IN BY THE SMELL.

STEP 4: BEAUTIFICATION

WHEN I CAME **OUT** OF THE SALT TREATMENT, MY BODY WAS TOTALLY SHRIVELLED UP LIKE A **RAISIN**.

TO RESTORE MY NATURALLY DEVASTATING **GOOD LOOKS**, I WAS MASSAGED ALL OVER WITH OILS AND PERFUMES.

I WAS ALSO STUFFED WITH **ONIONS** AND PERFUMED RAGS, FOR THAT PLUMP, **LIFE-LIKE** LOOK.

THEN I GOT A WIG, FAKE BEARD AND A BANG-UP MAKE-UP JOB, SO I COULD ENTER THE UNDERWORLD LOOKING LIKE A SUPERSTAR.

STEP 5: WRAPIFICATION

A MUMMY'S FAMOUS BANDAGES WERE MOSTLY THERE TO PROTECT THE NOW SUPER-DRY AND BRITTLE BODY FROM **SNAPPING**.

OOPS.

THE BANDAGES WERE LAYERED WITH PROTECTIVE AMULETS AND MAGIC CHARMS.

TET – BRINGS STABILITY AND BALANCE.

SCARAB – PROTECTS THE HEART.

ANKH – SYMBOL OF ETERNAL LIFE.

11 DAYS AND **300** METRES OF CAREFUL BANDAGING LATER, AND YOU HAVE ONE PERFECTLY PRESERVED PREMIUM POTENTATE READY TO ENTER ETERNITY.

AND NOW, MY NEXT GUEST IS THE WALL-BUILDING, BOOK-BURNING, EMPIRE-FOUNDING, SCHOLAR-BURYING, HISTORY-CHANGING, MODEL-SOLDIER-COLLECTING...

...FIRST EMPEROR OF CHINA! LET'S GIVE A WARM WELCOME TO...

QIN SHI HUANG DI!

QIN SHI HUANG DI
CHINESE EMPEROR
259 BCE – 210 BCE

YOU NAMED YOURSELF QIN SHI HUANG DI, WHICH LITERALLY TRANSLATES AS "TOTALLY AWESOME FIRST EMPEROR OF CHINA". ISN'T THAT BASICALLY LIKE ME CHANGING MY NAME TO "MOST AMAZING INTERVIEWER EVER"?

WELL, NOT QUITE. I MEAN, I REALLY WAS THE EMPEROR OF CHINA...

OOH. HARSH.

AT THAT TIME, CHINA WAS SPLIT UP INTO A BUNCH OF LITTLE KINGDOMS, ALL FIGHTING ONE ANOTHER FOR CONTROL.

MINE!

MINE!

BUT THEN **I** CAME ON THE SCENE! I **OBLITERATED** THEIR PUNY KINGDOMS AND TOOK OVER.

MINE.

WHICH, I THINK YOU'LL FIND, **IS** PRETTY AWESOME, MAKING THE NAME REALLY JUST A STATEMENT OF FACT.

OK. SURE. YOU'RE AWESOME. BUT WHY...

WHY!? BECAUSE THAT'S WHAT EMPERORS **DO!**

THE WHOLE **POINT** OF BEING AN EMPEROR IS TO TAKE OVER THE ENTIRE KNOWN WORLD AND FORCE EVERYONE TO YIELD TO YOUR INVINCIBLE WILL!

NO, I MEANT **WHY** WERE YOU ABLE TO BEAT EVERYONE ELSE? APART FROM "BEING AWESOME" OF COURSE. THEY ALL HAD ARMIES, TOO, DIDN'T THEY?

WELL, I **GUESS**. IF YOU CAN CALL A BUNCH OF **FANCY NOBLEMEN** RUNNING AROUND TRYING TO LOOK COOL AN **ARMY!**

I USED THE NEW TECHNOLOGY OF CHEAP **IRON** WEAPONS TO EQUIP A **MASSIVE**, RIGOROUSLY DISCIPLINED, **PROPER** ARMY, AND KICKED **ALL** THEIR BUMS!

AND I USED THE SAME PRINCIPLES OF MODERN ORGANISATION, BRUTAL PUNISHMENTS AND IRON **DISCIPLINE** TO ADMINISTER MY EMPIRE.

FOR EXAMPLE, PEOPLE ALL OVER THE PLACE WERE USING DIFFERENT MONEY, DIFFERENT MEASUREMENTS, DIFFERENT WRITING...

CAN YOU IMAGINE HOW **CONFUSING** THAT WAS!? I FORCED EVERYBODY TO USE **ONE SYSTEM**...

MINE.

BUT NOT EVERYONE THOUGHT **IMPERIALIST OPPRESSION** WAS AWESOME...

15

DIE, IMPERIALIST OPPRESSOR!

WHOA. NOT COOL!

NOT COOL AT ALL.

I HAD TO DO SOME **SERIOUS** RUNNING AWAY.

HAVE YOU **SEEN** THESE SHOES! NO **WAY** I WANT TO BE RUNNING, **FOR ANY** REASON!

IT WAS AT THIS POINT THAT YOU STARTED GETTING **PARANOID**.

HEY! THERE WERE PEOPLE TRYING TO KILL ME!

SURE, BUT YOU TOOK IT TO NEW HEIGHTS. YOU REFUSED TO SEE **ANYONE**.

I'M NOT HERE. LEAVE A MESSAGE...

YOU EMPLOYED A LEGION OF FOOD TASTERS.

SOUP'S OK...

SALAD'S OK...

MIGHT WANT TO AVOID DESSERT...

YOU BUILT A HUGE ARRAY OF PALACES AND MOVED AROUND CONSTANTLY TO AVOID STAYING IN THE SAME PLACE TWO NIGHTS IN A ROW.

AND YOU ORDERED ALL BOOKS ABOUT HISTORY BEFORE YOUR **REIGN** TO BE COLLECTED AND **BURNT!**

BAH! **HISTORY!** EVERY TIME I'D INTRODUCE A NEW REFORM, EVERYONE WOULD ALL BE LIKE "THINGS WERE **SOO** MUCH BETTER UNDER THE YELLOW EMPEROR"... OR "CONFUCIUS WOULDN'T HAVE WANTED IT DONE LIKE THAT..."

NO. I'M SORRY, BUT BURNING BOOKS IS **NEVER** AWESOME. THAT'S **THOUSANDS** OF YEARS OF FASCINATING CHINESE HISTORY THAT WE'LL NEVER KNOW ABOUT, ALL THANKS TO **YOUR** OVER-SENSITIVITY.

PFF! YOU SOUND JUST LIKE THOSE PESKY **CONFUCIAN SCHOLARS**. THEY USED TO SAY THE SAME THING...

SO I HAD 'EM ALL **BURIED ALIVE.**

YOU DON'T SCARE ME - I KNOW YOUR WEAKNESS. THE ONE THING YOU WERE **SO** AFRAID OF YOU BANNED ITS VERY MENTION...

WHAT!? NO...

NO NO NO NO LA LA LA I CAN'T HEAR YOU...

THAT'S RIGHT...

DEATH!

EEK!

YOU WERE SO PARANOID ABOUT YOUR **SO AWESOME** REIGN COMING TO AN END, YOU BUILT AN INSANELY HUGE TOMB, COMPLETE WITH A MASSIVE LIFE-SIZE MODEL ARMY TO PROTECT YOU IN THE NEXT LIFE...

YOU ALSO SENT OUT EXPEDITIONS TO FIND THE LEGENDARY **ISLAND OF THE IMMORTALS.**

I PROMISED THEM THAT IF THEY RETURNED **WITHOUT** THE IMMORTALS' SECRET OF LONGEVITY, I'D HAVE THEM ALL KILLED.

AND THEY NEVER RETURNED...

I KNOW. WEIRD...

YOU ALSO PAID A FORTUNE FOR MAGICAL **IMMORTALITY PILLS.**

TURNS OUT THE SECRET INGREDIENT WAS **POISON!** SO BASICALLY, YOU WERE KILLED BY TRYING TO AVOID DYING.

HOW VERY IRONIC...

THE EMPEROR'S TOMB

COVERING THE AREA OF A SMALL CITY, THE TOMB COMPLEX OF CHINA'S FIRST EMPEROR, **QIN SHI HUANG DI**, IS ONE OF THE WONDERS OF THE ANCIENT WORLD. CONSTRUCTED TO ENSURE HIS CONTINUED AWESOMENESS IN THE AFTERLIFE, IT CONTAINS OVER **8,000** STATUES, INCLUDING HIS WORLD-FAMOUS, LIFE-SIZE **TERRACOTTA ARMY!**

AW YEAH! NOW **THAT'S** SOME SWEET DIGS!

NEW MODEL ARMY

THE MASSIVE ARMY OF TERRACOTTA WARRIORS STANDS GUARD IN FRONT OF THE EMPEROR'S TOMB.

FOOTSOLDIERS MAKE UP THE BULK OF THE ARMY, WITH OVER **6,000** SCULPTURES.

CITY OF DEATH

THE HUGE PITS HOUSING THE ARMY ARE DWARFED BY THE MASSIVE SCALE OF THE CITY-SIZED TOMB COMPLEX ITSELF.

OUTER CITY: HOUSES THE TOMBS OF ELITE HIGH OFFICIALS.

INNER CITY: CONTAINS THE ENORMOUS FUNERARY PALACE OF THE EMPEROR, BURIED BENEATH A MAN-MADE PYRAMID OF EARTH BIG ENOUGH TO RIVAL THE PYRAMIDS OF EGYPT.

- RARE ANIMALS
- ROYAL OFFICIALS
- PLEASURE GARDEN
- STONE ARMOUR
- TERRACOTTA ARMY
- WRESTLERS
- ROYAL HORSES
- PALACE
- BRONZE CHARIOTS
- MASS GRAVE OF WORKERS WHO DIED DURING CONSTRUCTION

PALACE OF SHADOWS

INSIDE HIS UNDERGROUND PALACE, THE EMPEROR RESTS IN A MASSIVE HALL THE SIZE OF A FOOTBALL PITCH.

THE CEILING IS COVERED WITH A JEWELLED MAP OF THE HEAVENS.

ON THE FLOOR IS LAID OUT A MAP OF HIS ENTIRE EMPIRE, WITH SCALE MODELS OF ALL HIS PALACES.

THE RIVERS AND SEAS, DESIGNED IN SUCH A WAY THAT THEY REALLY FLOW, ARE FILLED WITH DEADLY POISONOUS **LIQUID MERCURY.**

MINE! ALL MINE!

MWA HA HA HA HA!

SUPPOSEDLY, THE TREASURES ARE GUARDED BY HIDDEN CROSSBOW BOOBY-TRAPS, RIGGED TO SHOOT ANY WOULD-BE TOMB RAIDERS...

YEAH BUT, YOU'RE STILL DEAD.

ACTUALLY, WHEN YOU THINK ABOUT IT LIKE THAT, THE WHOLE THING SEEMS KINDA SAD...

OFFICERS ARE MARKED OUT BY THEIR TALL HEADDRESSES.

ARCHERS CROUCH READY FOR BATTLE. LIKE ALL THE SOLDIERS, THEIR WEAPONS HAVE LONG SINCE ROTTED AWAY.

CAVALRYMEN WITH THEIR SHORT, LIGHT ARMOUR STAND WITH THEIR PRIZED HORSES.

NOW FADED, THE WARRIORS WERE ORIGINALLY PAINTED IN BRIGHT COLOURS!

EACH STATUE WAS MODELLED ON ONE OF THE EMPEROR'S REAL-LIFE ELITE SOLDIERS.

EVEN THE HAIRSTYLES!

BURIED ALIVE

THE EMPEROR WAS **SO AFRAID** OF THE BUILDERS REVEALING THE SECRETS OF THE TOMB'S DEFENCES THAT, WHILE THEY WERE PUTTING IN THE LAST FINISHING TOUCHES, THEY WERE ALL SHUT UP INSIDE!

SLAM!

BURIED TREASURES

IN ADDITION TO THE TERRACOTTA WARRIORS, ARCHAEOLOGISTS HAVE RECENTLY DISCOVERED ALL SORTS OF OTHER FANTASTIC TREASURES IN THE PALACE COMPLEX.

LIKE A **MASSIVE** SUIT OF **STONE ARMOUR**. TOO HEAVY TO WEAR, IT IS THOUGHT TO BE DESIGNED TO PROTECT THE EMPEROR FROM UNDERWORLD SPIRITS.

HE HAD A **PLEASURE GARDEN** FILLED WITH LIFELIKE STATUES OF HIS FAVOURITE MUSICIANS AND EXOTIC BIRDS.

RECENTLY UNEARTHED: A TEAM OF **BRONZE WRESTLERS**. LIKE HAVING **WWE** IN YOUR LIVING ROOM!

LUCKY FIND

THE TERRACOTTA WARRIORS, AND THE ENTIRE TOMB COMPLEX, WERE DISCOVERED BY **ACCIDENT** BY THREE FARMERS, WHILE THEY WERE DIGGING A WELL...

BEHIND THE TOMB IS A SET OF **BRONZE CHARIOTS**, COMPLETE WITH HORSES AND DRIVERS, READY FOR A SIGHTSEEING TRIP AROUND THE KINGDOM.

YEAH! VROOM VROOM! LET'S GO!

THE EMPEROR'S **CENTRAL PALACE MOUND** IS YET TO BE OPENED. NO ONE KNOWS FOR SURE WHAT AMAZING STUFF IT HOLDS.

EXCEPT MEEE!

AND I'M NOT TELLING!

LET'S MEET THE WOMAN WHO **STOLE THE HEARTS** OF ROME'S GREATEST LEADERS. HISTORY'S MOST EVIL WOMAN, OR A **BRILLIANT SURVIVOR** IN A DIFFICULT TIME? **YOU DECIDE!**

IT'S **THE LAST PHARAOH OF EGYPT,** QUEEN OF THE NILE...

CLEOPATRA!

CLEOPATRA
PHARAOH OF EGYPT
69 BCE–
30 BCE

CLEO, YOU SHARED THE RULE OF EGYPT WITH YOUR LITTLE BROTHER (AND HUSBAND) **PTOLEMY XIII.** ONLY ONE PROBLEM...

YOU DIDN'T LIKE TO SHARE!

WELL, COME ON! I WAS THE MOST CAPABLE WOMAN OF MY AGE! I SPOKE **9 LANGUAGES!** I WAS AN EXPERT IN **SCIENCE** AND **PHILOSOPHY!** I'D BEEN TRAINED TO RULE SINCE CHILDHOOD...

MY BROTHER WAS A SNOTTY **10**-YEAR-OLD WITH AN ATTITUDE PROBLEM.

THHP!!

SO I DID WHAT **ANY** SENSIBLE OLDER SISTER/ WIFE WOULD DO...

YOU STARTED A CIVIL WAR TO GET RID OF HIM.

WHICH DIDN'T GO SO GREAT, ACTUALLY. HE WAS A BOY, AND ALL THE OTHER BOYS AT COURT BACKED HIM OVER ME.

I NEEDED HELP. PREFERABLY FROM SOMEONE WITH AN **ARMY.** AND THEN I HEARD THAT ROMAN RUMP-KICKER **JULIUS CAESAR** WAS IN EGYPT...

I HAD TO SEE HIM! BUT WITH MY BROTHER STILL HUNTING FOR ME, I ALSO HAD TO BE **SNEAKY...**

KEEP AN EYE OUT FOR CLEOPATRA!

NO WAY SHE'S GETTING IN HERE!

A NEW CARPET FOR CAESAR!?

RIGHT THIS WAY!

CAESAR FELL HEAD OVER HEELS IN LOVE WITH YOU AND, WITH HIS BACKING, YOU BECAME THE MOST POWERFUL WOMAN IN THE WORLD!

JUST TO MAKE SURE, YOU HAD YOUR BROTHER AND ALL YOUR OTHER SIBLINGS KILLED!

THAT'S PRETTY RUTHLESS.

AW! THANKS!

AT **LAST,** I COULD RUN THINGS **MY** WAY!

UNDER MY **ENLIGHTENED RULE,** EGYPT ENTERED A NEW GOLDEN AGE OF PEACE AND PROSPERITY.

MEANWHILE, CAESAR HAD **ALSO** DESTROYED HIS ENEMIES AND BECOME THE UNDISPUTED MASTER OF ROME.

AS PART OF HIS CELEBRATIONS, HE HAD A MASSIVE **GOLD STATUE** OF ME PUT UP IN HIS NEW TEMPLE OF **VENUS**, THE GODDESS OF LOVE.

TOO MUCH BLING?

NO SUCH THING...

HOW ROMANTIC!

HM. WELL, ACTUALLY THAT'S KIND OF WHERE THE TROUBLE STARTED...

SEE, IN EGYPT, WORSHIPPING STATUES OF PEOPLE WAS PRETTY NORMAL. AS **PHARAOH**, I WAS KIND OF A GOD-KING THERE ALREADY.

CAESAR WAS WONDERING IF **HE** COULD GET AWAY WITH MAKING HIMSELF INTO A SORT OF **ROMAN** GOD-KING, SO THIS WAS ONE WAY OF TESTING HOW THE ROMANS FELT ABOUT THE SUBJECT.

TURNS OUT, THEY **HATED** THE IDEA. SO MUCH SO, IN FACT, THEY **STABBED HIM TO DEATH.**

AND **HERE'S** WHAT WE THINK OF YOUR STUPID STATUE!

OUCH! SOME PEOPLE SAY IT WITH FLOWERS..

THE ROMANS SAY IT WITH **STABBINGS.**

YOU NEEDED ANOTHER ROMAN PROTECTOR, AND **FAST!** YOU HOOKED CAESAR'S SECOND-IN-COMMAND, **MARK ANTONY.**

SO YOU MANAGED TO BEGUILE NOT ONE, BUT **TWO** OF THE MOST POWERFUL MEN IN THE WORLD, IN QUICK SUCCESSION, WITH YOUR LEGENDARY **BEAUTY**...

HM. I PREFER TO THINK IT WAS DOWN TO MY FASCINATING **PERSONALITY**...

AFTER ALL, MY **CHARM** WAS **ALSO** LEGENDARY!

IT'S SAID THAT YOU HAD "A THOUSAND FORMS OF FLATTERY"!

WOW! THAT'S IMPRESSIVE! YOU'VE OBVIOUSLY DONE YOUR HOMEWORK!

OH THANK YOU... I TRY...

PLUS, I WAS STINKIN' RICH!

ANTONY ONCE BET ME I COULDN'T SPEND A MILLION POUNDS ON ONE MEAL...

OH YEAH?

CHALLENGE ACCEPTED!

ENORMOUS PEARL

VINEGAR

PLOP!

PEARLS **DISSOLVE** IN VINEGAR...

DOOK DOOK DOOK

CLAP CLAP

ROME DECLARED WAR ON YOU, CLAIMING THAT YOUR LIFE OF LUXURY HAD MADE ANTONY **SOFT**, AND THAT YOU WANTED TO TAKE OVER THEIR EMPIRE.

BUT I DID!

WELL, ANTONY'S SOLDIERS CERTAINLY BELIEVED IT. THEY **DESERTED** HIM EN MASSE AND JOINED HIS ENEMY'S ARMY.

GUYS!

COME BACK!

GUYS!

SO LONG...

SOFTY!

DESERTED AND DEFEATED, HE FELL ON HIS SWORD. EXCEPT HE **BOTCHED** THAT TOO...

THIS... DOESN'T SEEM TO HAVE WORKED. COULD SOMEONE HELP ME OUT HERE...?

THE ROMANS WERE COMING TO TAKE YOU PRISONER.

BUT I WOULDN'T GIVE THEM THE SATISFACTION!

I ENDED MY LIFE WITH A POISONOUS ASP!

G-ASP!

OH PLEASE TELL ME YOU DID NOT JUST SAY THAT...

THIS NEXT DUDE HAS BECOME THE ULTIMATE SYMBOL OF THE DECADENT GLAMOUR OF **IMPERIAL ROME**. BUT HE'S ALSO **CONSISTENTLY** RATED AS ONE OF THE **WORST** WORLD LEADERS OF **ALL TIME!**

PLEASE WELCOME HISTORY'S ORIGINAL **NECKBEARD**, IT'S THE SINGING EMPEROR...

NERO!

NERO
ROMAN EMPEROR
37–68

HEH – THAT'S FUNNY... IT ALMOST SOUNDED LIKE YOU SAID "WORST" THERE INSTEAD OF "BEST".

AS IN "BEST WORLD LEADER OF ALL TIME..."

UH, YEAH... SORRY – THAT'S... NOT REALLY THE VERDICT OF HISTORY, WHICH REGARDS YOU AS AN **INDULGENT BULLY** WHO FIDDLED WHILE ROME BURNED.

AW WHAT!?

OK, FIRST OFF – FIDDLES HADN'T BEEN INVENTED YET. I PLAYED THE **LYRE**.

TOTALLY **SHREDDED** ON IT TOO...

I TRIED RIGGING A SPECIAL **COLLAPSIBLE BOAT** TO SINK HER AT SEA, BUT SHE JUST SWAM TO SHORE, AND THE GUYS I SENT TO **FINISH** THE JOB KILLED THE WRONG WOMAN!

GET 'ER!

AAAAGH!

SO IN THE END, I JUST HAD HER STABBED.

YOU MONSTER!

YEAH, DUDE. BAD ENOUGH YOU KILLED YOUR **OWN MOTHER**, BUT AFTER ALL THE MURDERING SHE DID FOR YOU... WELL, THAT'S JUST **UNGRATEFUL**.

OH, DON'T GET ME WRONG. I FELT TOTALLY **GUILTY** ABOUT IT...

FOR YEARS I WAS SURE SHE WAS **HAUNTING** ME, AS PUNISHMENT FOR MY HEINOUS CRIMES...

NEROO

NEROOOO...

NEROOOO... YOU SUUUCK...

YES, YES. **THANK** YOU, MOTHER. THAT'S YOUR BIT OVER WITH NOW...

WITH DEAR MOTHER OUT OF THE WAY, I WAS FINALLY READY TO BECOME THE EMPEROR I'D ALWAYS DREAMED OF BEING... A **SINGING** ONE!

I TOOK TO THE STAGE, **WOWING** AUDIENCES WHEREVER I WENT WITH MY POWERFUL, MOVING SINGING AND LYRE-PLAYING.

YOU HAD THE **DOORS LOCKED** SO NO ONE COULD LEAVE. IT GOT SO BAD, PEOPLE ACTUALLY **FAKED BEING DEAD**, JUST SO THEY WOULD GET CARRIED OUT.

BAH! PHILISTINES!

ANYWAY, ISN'T A ROMAN EMPEROR SUPPOSED TO HAVE MORE... **VIOLENT** HOBBIES? LIKE DESTROYING THE ENEMIES OF ROME?

WHEN YOU'RE A GENIUS LIKE ME, MUSIC ISN'T A **HOBBY**, IT'S A **WAY OF LIFE**...

DESPITE YOUR MUSICAL "WAY OF LIFE", YOU WERE SURPRISINGLY POPULAR, THANKS TO YOUR LAVISH SPENDING ON GLADIATORIAL GAMES.

HEH. GOOD OL' NERO!

AAARRGH!

AT LEAST, UNTIL THE **GREAT FIRE OF ROME** BURNT HUGE SWATHES OF THE ETERNAL CITY TO THE GROUND.

THAT WASN'T MY FAULT!

MAYBE NOT, BUT YOU SURE TOOK ADVANTAGE OF IT TO BUILD A MASSIVE PALACE ON THE STILL-SMOULDERING RUINS OF PEOPLE'S HOMES!

...AND WE'LL PUT MY PRIVATE BATHS HERE...

WHICH MIGHT BE WHAT STARTED THE RUMOUR THAT YOU WERE HAPPILY FIDDLING — SORRY, LYRE-ING, WHILE THE CITY WENT UP IN SMOKE.

BURN, BABY, BURN!

IT WAS A P.R. DISAST... THEY WERE EVEN SAYI... DID IT! I HAD TO FI... SOMEONE ELSE TO PIN...THE BLAME ON!

SOMEONE PEOPLE ALREADY HATED...

SOMEONE LIKE THE **CHRISTIANS**, A BUNCH OF DODGY FOREIGNERS WITH WEIRDO RELIGIOUS PRACTICES, LIKE CARING FOR THE POOR.

YOU HAD THEM ROUNDED UP, PUBLICLY TORTURED AND EXECUTED FOR THEIR "CRIMES".

HA HA! ROME IS AVENGED!

BUT EVEN **THAT** BACKFIRED WHEN YOUR EXCESSIVE CRUELTY MADE PEOPLE **PITY** THE CHRISTIANS INSTEAD.

DID YOU **SEE** WHAT NERO DID!?

I **KNOW!** THAT'S BARBARIC!

BUT IN THE END, IT WASN'T YOUR HORRIBLE CRUELTY, YOUR MURDERING YOUR OWN MUM, OR EVEN YOUR AWFUL SINGING THAT DID YOU IN, BUT YOUR CRIPPLING **TAX POLICY.**

HEY, GOLDEN PALACES AND GIANT STATUES OF YOURSELF DON'T COME CHEAP!

AND THE PEOPLE GOT SICK OF BEING **TAXED** TO PAY FOR THEM, AND **REVOLTED!**

DESERTED BY MY FRIENDS AND HUNTED BY MY OWN LEGIONS, I TOOK MY OWN LIFE, SILENCING THIS BEAUTIFUL VOICE FOREVER.

UNTIL NOW!

...

COME **ON!** I CAN **SEE** YOU BREATHING!

AND NOW, THE **EMPEROR** **STRIKES BACK!** MY GUEST MAY HAVE NO **NOSE**, BUT HE KNOWS HOW TO SOW WOES AS HE MOWS DOWN HIS FOES! (TRY SAYING THAT THREE TIMES FAST.)

IT'S THE **BYZANTINE BUTTKICKER**...

JUSTINIAN II!

JUSTINIAN II
BYZANTINE EMPEROR
c. 669–711

JUSTINIAN, YOU WERE CROWNED HEAD OF THE **BYZANTINE** EMPIRE NOT ONCE BUT **TWICE**, RETURNING TO POWER IN A BLOODY, VENGEANCE-FUELLED ODYSSEY OF **VIOLENCE**.

UH, I THINK YOU MEAN **ROMAN** EMPIRE...

PFF. I THOUGHT THIS WAS SUPPOSED TO BE A **HISTORY** BOOK...

NO, NO — I **KNOW** THAT! HISTORIANS CALL THE LATER ROMAN EMPIRE **BYZANTINE**, AFTER THE CAPITAL MOVED TO **BYZANTIUM**.

I THINK YOU MEAN **CONSTANTINOPLE**...

YESSS I KNOW, THE EMPEROR **CONSTANTINE** RENAMED BYZANTIUM AFTER HIMSELF.

NO **WONDER** YOU BYZANTINES HAVE A REPUTATION FOR MAKING THINGS COMPLICATED...

YOU MEAN ROMANS...

I KNOW WHAT I MEAN!

WHATEVER YOU WANNA CALL THEM, THE BYZANTINES STILL KINDA HATED YOUR **GUTS**.

HM.

THAT'S TRUE...

FOR SOME REASON, THEY **OBJECTED** TO ME USING ALL THE EMPIRE'S TAXES TO BUILD GIANT **STATUES** OF MYSELF...

WHICH MADE ME **SO** UNPOPULAR A DISGRUNTLED GENERAL NAMED **LEONTIUS** WAS ABLE TO REBEL AND SEIZE THE THRONE!

IN A BIZARRE MIX OF CRUELTY AND MERCY, HE **CUT OFF MY NOSE**, AND SENT ME INTO **EXILE**.

SINCE THE BYZANTINES WERE CHRISTIANS, THEY TRIED TO AVOID KILLING.

OR AT LEAST, KILLING **EMPERORS**...

I GUESS THEIR IDEA WAS THAT NO ONE WOULD FOLLOW A NOSELESS EMPEROR...

PFF! SUCKERS!

THE MOMENT I ARRIVED AT MY NEW HOME (A TINY TOWN ON THE FAR COAST OF THE **BLACK SEA**) I STARTED PLOTTING MY RETURN TO POWER.

HEY GUYS! WHO WANTS TO JOIN A REBELLION?

THE TOWN ELDERS GOT WIND OF YOUR PLANS AND WARNED THE EMPEROR LEONTIUS...

I THINK YOU MEAN **TIBERIUS**, ACTUALLY...

OH, COME **ON**!

YUP. WHILE I WAS AWAY, LEONTIUS **ALSO** GOT DEPOSED, DE-NOSED AND A NEW EMPEROR TOOK HIS PLACE.

IT'S NOT **THAT** DIFFICULT. THE POINT IS, THE NEW, EVIL, **FALSE** EMPEROR HAD DECIDED THAT THE GOOD, HANDSOME, **TRUE** EMPEROR (THAT'S ME) WAS TOO DANGEROUS TO **LIVE**, NOSE OR NO NOSE.

SO YOU GAVE THE EMPEROR'S MEN THE **SLIP** AND ESCAPED THE EMPIRE, VENTURING INTO THE LANDS OF THE **BARBARIANS**.

ROMAN Byzantine EMPIRE

THE KING OF A TRIBE OF NOMADS CALLED THE **KHAZARS**, AGREED TO HELP (I PROMISED HIM MASSIVE **REWARDS** WHEN I REGAINED MY THRONE).

AND **HE** DIDN'T HAVE A PROBLEM WITH THE WHOLE **NO-NOSE** THING?

ACTUALLY, IT KIND OF **HELPED**...

THINK ABOUT IT: SOME GUY SHOWS UP CLAIMING TO BE THE **DEPOSED ROMAN EMPEROR** — WOULD **YOU** BELIEVE HIM?

BUT EVERYONE KNEW THE STORY ABOUT MY **DE-NOSIFICATION**. I GUESS THEY FIGURED NO ONE WOULD GO **THAT** FAR JUST TO IMPERSONATE ME.

TO CEMENT OUR DEAL, THE KHAZAR KING MARRIED ME TO HIS SISTER, A BARBARIAN PRINCESS WITH A NAME **SO UNPRONOUNCEABLE**, I JUST GAVE HER A ROMAN ONE: **THEODORA**.

BUT THEN SHE WARNED ME THAT HER BROTHER HAD **DOUBLE-CROSSED** ME, AND WAS SENDING MEN TO TAKE MY HEAD TO THE EMPEROR.

I **STRANGLED** THE WOULD-BE ASSASSINS WITH MY **BARE HANDS**, BUT NOW I WAS ON THE RUN AGAIN.

AS I SAILED AWAY, A VIOLENT STORM BLEW UP. THE SAILORS WERE TERRIFIED IT WAS THE WRATH OF **GOD**.

AAH! IT'S BECAUSE OF YOUR QUEST FOR **VENGEANCE**! PROMISE TO FORGIVE YOUR ENEMIES — MAYBE GOD WILL FORGIVE **US**!

WHAT!? NO WAY! IN FACT, IF I DON'T KILL EVERY LAST **ONE** OF THEM, MAY GOD **DROWN** ME RIGHT NOW!

WHAT!? IT'S NOT LIKE I WAS GOING TO **TURN THE OTHER CHEEK** OR SOMETHING...

ANYWAY, WE SURVIVED. SO I FIGURED GOD **BACKED** MY PLANS TO RETAKE THE THRONE AND ENACT **HOMICIDAL REVENGE**.

BUT I STILL NEEDED AN ARMY, SO I TRIED MY LUCK WITH **ANOTHER** BARBARIAN KING, THIS TIME THE KING OF THE **BULGARS**.

HE AGREED TO HELP IN RETURN FOR BEING DECLARED CAESAR (A BYZANTINE TITLE, LIKE A DUKE), PLUS A **MOUNTAIN** OF CASH, AND WE MARCHED ON CONSTANTINOPLE.

BEAR IN MIND, THE WALLS OF CONSTANTINOPLE WERE THE LARGEST AND STRONGEST IN THE ANCIENT WORLD.

OH, COME ON, GUYS!

NO WAY! YOU'LL JUST KILL US ALL!

WELL, TRUE...

BUT THEN WE FOUND A **SEWER**. I DIVED IN HEAD-FIRST, AND LED MY MEN THROUGH A RIVER OF **POOP** TO RETAKE MY CROWN.

RAAH!

YOU SEIZED THE PALACE, HAD A **BATH**, AND THEN UNLEASHED YOUR LEGENDARY **PROGRAMME** OF **PAYBACK**...

CULMINATING IN A **TRIUMPHAL ROMAN GAMES**, WHICH YOU ENJOYED WHILE USING **BOTH** OF THE EX-EMPERORS (LEONTIUS **AND** TIBERIUS) AS **FOOTSTOOLS**.

SOLID GOLD REPLACEMENT NOSE

SO YOU DIDN'T KILL THEM?

OH, I KILLED THEM AFTERWARDS...

SEE. NOT **EVERYTHING'S** COMPLICATED...

THE WALLED CITY

EMPEROR JUSTINIAN II GOT INTO A SPOT OF BOTHER WITH THOSE WONDERS OF THE ANCIENT WORLD, THE **WALLS OF CONSTANTINOPLE**. I'VE ASKED HIM TO GIVE US SOME MORE FACTS ABOUT THOSE **FORMIDABLE FORTIFICATIONS**.

YUP — THE **THEODOSIAN WALLS**, AS WE BYZANTINES LIKE TO CALL THEM (THEY WERE BUILT BY THE EMPEROR THEODOSIUS) WERE THE LARGEST AND MOST IMPRESSIVE DEFENSIVE WALLS OF THE ANCIENT WORLD. GREAT WHEN YOU WERE ON THE INSIDE. NOT SO MUCH WHEN YOU WERE OUTSIDE TRYING TO GET IN.

DEFENSIVE STRUCTURES:

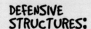

THE FIRST LINE OF DEFENCE WAS THE **MOAT**. 20M WIDE AND 10M DEEP. THIS MADE IT HARD TO GET SIEGE TOWERS OR BATTERING RAMS ANYWHERE **NEAR** THE WALLS THEMSELVES.

IF THEY MADE IT ACROSS THE MOAT, ATTACKERS NEXT HAD TO FACE THE 9M-TALL **OUTER WALLS**. FROM HERE, DEFENDERS COULD RAIN DOWN ARROWS ON THE ATTACKING ARMY.

LINE OF DEFENCE:

THE THEODESIAN WALLS RAN FOR **35** UNINTERRUPTED MILES, FROM THE GOLDEN HORN TO THE SEA OF MARMARA, SEALING OFF THE CITY COMPLETELY FROM ANY ATTACK BY LAND.

SMALLER, BUT STILL IMPRESSIVE, WALLS ALSO SEALED OFF THE SEA, RENDERING THE CITY VIRTUALLY IMPREGNABLE.

FOILED BY THE WALL

IT WASN'T JUST ME! THESE ARE JUST SOME OF THE YOUNG HOPEFULS WHO WERE...

ATTILA THE HUN: TOOK ONE LOOK AT THE WALLS, AND DECIDED TO ATTACK ROME INSTEAD.

THE AVARS: BEATEN SO BADLY, THEY BELIEVED **GOD** WAS ON THE BYZANTINE SIDE.

THE ARABS: CONQUERED MOST OF BYZANTINE TERRITORY, BUT WERE UNABLE TO CAPTURE THE CITY.

THE CRUSADERS: MANAGED TO SACK THE CITY, BUT ONLY BY GOING OVER THE LOWER, WEAKER SEA WALLS.

THE BYZANTINES: TRIED SEVERAL TIMES TO GET THE CITY BACK FROM THE CRUSADERS, BUT COULDN'T BREAK THROUGH THEIR **OWN** WALLS! SUCCEEDED BY WAITING UNTIL THE CRUSADERS LEFT!

ANYONE WHO SOMEHOW SCALED THE FORMIDABLE OUTER WALL WOULD FIND THEMSELVES TRAPPED AND SURROUNDED IN THE **PERIBOLOS**, THE **15**M-WIDE ENCLOSED WALKWAY BETWEEN THE WALLS.

AND IF THEY SOMEHOW CLEARED THE PERIBOLOS, ATTACKERS WERE NOW FACED WITH THE MOST MASSIVE DEFENSIVE STRUCTURE OF THE ANCIENT WORLD, THE **INNER WALLS**. **5**M THICK AND **12**M HIGH, STUDDED WITH **96** MASSIVE TOWERS, THE WALLS WERE LARGE ENOUGH FOR DEFENDERS TO MOUNT CATAPULTS AND EVEN CANNON, TO RAIN TERROR ON THE ARMY OUTSIDE.

THE WALL FALLS:

CONSTANTINOPLE'S AMAZING WALLS FINALLY FELL TO THE MASSIVE CANNONS OF THE TURKISH SULTAN **MEHMED II** IN **1453**, MARKING THE END OF ALMOST **1,500** YEARS OF THE **ROMAN EMPIRE**.

MY NEXT GUEST IS THE **DESTROYER** OF THE **DESSERT** COURSE, THE **CONFECTIONERY-CREMATING** COMMANDER OF THE ANGLO-SAXONS...

IT'S THE KING WHO BURNED THE CAKES...

ALFRED THE GREAT!

ALFRED
THE GREAT
KING OF WESSEX
849–899

ALFRED, YOU'RE POSSIBLY BEST REMEMBERED TODAY FOR A CERTAIN **CULINARY DISASTER**...

OH, COME ON!

I TAKE MY EYE OFF THE BALL **ONE TIME** AND **THAT'S** WHAT PEOPLE REMEMBER!?

WHAT ABOUT, OH I DON'T KNOW, **SAVING ENGLAND** FROM HORDES OF **RAVENING VIKINGS**!?

LET ME TELL YOU ABOUT **VIKINGS**! REMORSELESS, UNSTOPPABLE **KILLING MACHINES**. THEIR STRANGE PAGAN GODS PROMISED A SPECIAL HEAVEN TO ANY WARRIOR WHO DIED FIGHTING, WHICH MADE THEM TERRIFYINGLY **FEARLESS** IN BATTLE.

FOR YEARS THEY'D BEEN PLUNDERING THE COASTLINE, APPEARING LITERALLY OUT **OF THE BLUE** IN THEIR LONGBOATS.

BUT THAT WAS JUST THE START OF IT! INITIALLY, THEY'D JUST RAIDED THE COASTS, BUT NOW THEY WERE ATTACKING **INLAND**, AND THEY WERE PLANNING TO **STAY**!

NOW, I SHOULD POINT OUT, AT THIS TIME THERE WAS NO "ENGLAND" - INSTEAD THERE WERE MULTIPLE ANGLO-SAXON KINGDOMS, ALL FIGHTING AMONGST THEMSELVES.

Northumbria

Mercia East Anglia

Britons

Wessex

UNWILLING TO UNITE, THEY WERE CONQUERED ONE BY ONE, UNTIL ONLY **ONE** REMAINED... THE MIGHTY KINGDOM OF **WESSEX**!

Vikings

Wessex

BLOODY BUT UNBOWED, SOLITARY LIGHT IN THE DARKNESS, LAST BASTION OF HOPE FOR ANGLO-SAXON CHRISTENDOM...

YOU WERE GETTING CREAMED.

YEP.

THE VIKINGS HAD DESTROYED MY ARMY, CAPTURED MY CASTLE AND FORCED ME TO FLEE INTO THE **FENS** (A SORT OF GIANT MARSH).

BUT FEAR NOT! THIS WAS NOT DEFEAT, JUST A MERE SETBACK! YOU SEE, THIS WAS WHEN I BURNT THE CAKES...

AND THE VIKINGS WERE SO HORRIFIED BY THE LOW STANDARDS OF ANGLO-SAXON BAKING THAT THEY ALL WENT HOME IN DISGUST?

NOW YOU'RE JUST BEING FACETIOUS.

I WAS HIDING OUT, IN DISGUISE, IN A PEASANT'S HUT. EVEN **THEY** DIDN'T KNOW WHO I WAS...

OI, YOU! KEEP AN EYE ON THEM CAKES WILLYA?

AS I GAZED DEEP INTO THE FIRE, BROODING ON MY DEFEATS, I STARTED TO THINK ABOUT WHY THE VIKINGS KEPT WINNING...

I MEAN, OK, THEY WERE REALLY SCARY, BUT THERE WAS MORE TO IT THAN THAT...

THEY WERE ALSO REALLY **FAST**. THEY WERE MASTERS OF SUDDENLY SHOWING UP RIGHT WHERE THEY WEREN'T EXPECTED.

COO-EE!

WHILE MY SOLDIERS WERE PRIMARILY FARMERS. IT COULD TAKE **WEEKS** FOR THEM TO GET FROM THEIR FARMS TO WHEREVER THE BATTLE WAS.

BY WHICH TIME, THE VIKINGS COULD HAVE ATTACKED, KILLED EVERYONE, HAD A PARTY, AND THEY'D **STILL** BE MILES AWAY!

BUT IT WAS THERE, IN THAT PEASANT'S HUT, STARING INTO THE FIRE, THAT I SAW HOW TO FINALLY BEAT THEM...

BURHS!

COME AGAIN?

BURHS! FORTIFIED TOWNS. IT'S WHERE YOUR MODERN WORD **BOROUGH** COMES FROM. AS IN EDINBURGH. OR MIDDLESBROUGH.

ALL ACROSS THE KINGDOM I WOULD SET UP THESE WALLED TOWNS OR BURHS. HALF THE PEOPLE COULD WORK IN THE FIELDS, WHILE THE OTHER HALF KEPT GUARD.

IT MEANT I ALWAYS HAD SOLDIERS WAITING TO FIGHT ANYWHERE THE VIKINGS SHOWED UP!

WITH THIS NEW SYSTEM I WOULD FILL THE LAND WITH THE SMOKE OF A THOUSAND VIKING **FUNERAL PYRES**...

HEY, WAIT A MINUTE — SOMETHING **IS** BURNING...

ARGH! DUDE! YOU HAD **ONE** JOB!

SO WHAT HAPPENED THEN?

THEN, I RALLIED MY SCATTERED FORCES FOR THE GREATEST BATTLE OF...

NO, I MEAN WITH THE CAKES...

LIKE, WERE YOU ALL "I'M **THE KING!** I **DON'T HAVE TIME FOR TRIVIAL PASTRIES!"** OR DID YOU JUST APOLOGISE AND GO OUT TO BUY SOME FRESH ONES?

HISTORY DOESN'T SAY.

IN FACT, IT'S ENTIRELY POSSIBLE THE WHOLE THING WAS INVENTED BY LATER MEDIEVAL SCHOLARS, BUT LET'S NOT LET **FACTS** GET IN THE WAY OF A GOOD STORY, EH?

AS I WAS **SAYING**... I RALLIED MY SCATTERED FORCES FOR THE MOST IMPORTANT FIGHT OF MY LIFE: THE BATTLE OF **EDINGTON!**

FILLED WITH FRESH RESOLVE, WE VANQUISHED THE VIKINGS AND FORCED THEM TO MAKE PEACE.

THEN BEGAN THE **REAL** WORK OF REBUILDING A STABLE, PROSPEROUS, WELL-EDUCATED KINGDOM FOR FUTURE GENERATIONS TO INHERIT.

AND, IN THE PEACE AND STABILITY **I** CREATED, MY SUCCESSORS WERE ABLE TO RECONQUER AND UNITE ALL THE ANGLO-SAXON KINGDOMS INTO ONE, GREAT, **ANGLE-LAND.**

SO THERE YOU GO. A BAD BAKER, BUT A PRETTY DECENT KING...

OMG! IT WAS **ONE TIME!**

41

THE DARK ISLAND

KING ALFRED THE GREAT IS BACK TO SHED LIGHT ON DARK AGES BRITAIN!

ACTUALLY, I PREFER THE TERM EARLY MIDDLE AGES. "DARK AGES" MAKES IT SOUND LIKE WE WERE ALL UNCIVILISED SAVAGES.

EUROPE WAS A COMPLEX NETWORK OF DIFFERENT PEOPLES, ALL WITH THEIR OWN UNIQUE HISTORIES, LANGUAGES AND CULTURES, ALL STRUGGLING FOR SUPREMACY AND SURVIVAL.

Britons

THIS WAS THE ROMANS' NAME FOR THE NATIVE PEOPLE. THEY SPOKE THE CELTIC LANGUAGE THAT SPREAD THROUGHOUT EUROPE AT THE START OF THE IRON AGE.

ORIGINALLY PAGANS WHOSE PRIESTS (DRUIDS) CONDUCTED HUMAN SACRIFICES!

THE BRITONS MOSTLY CONVERTED TO CHRISTIANITY DURING THE ROMAN OCCUPATION.

Irish and Picts

THESE GROUPS OF BRITONS WERE NEVER CONQUERED BY THE ROMANS, AND SO KEPT THEIR OWN RULERS AND THEIR OWN CULTURE.

Romano-Britons

BRITONS WHO EVENTUALLY BECAME PROUD ROMAN CITIZENS, SPEAKING LATIN AND ENJOYING THE PEACE AND SECURITY OF THE ROMAN EMPIRE.

BUT WHEN THE ROMAN ARMY LEFT, THE ROMANO-BRITONS HAD GOTTEN SO USED TO ROMAN PROTECTION, THEY COULDN'T REALLY DEFEND THEM-SELVES ANY MORE...

SO THEY HIRED A BUNCH OF TOUGH BARBARIANS FROM GERMANY CALLED SAXONS TO PROTECT THEM FROM IRISH AND PICTISH RAIDERS. SMART MOVE, RIGHT?

WHAT COULD POSSIBLY GO WRONG!?

Anglo-Saxons

GERMANIC-SPEAKING TRIBES FROM THE **ANGELN** PENINSULA (DENMARK) AND **SAXONY** (NORTH GERMANY), THESE BARBARIANS WERE THEMSELVES BEING PUSHED OUT BY EVEN **TOUGHER** BARBARIANS FROM THE EAST!

BROUGHT IN TO HELP **DEFEND** THE NATIVE BRITONS, THE **SAXONS** LIKED IT SO MUCH, THEY STAYED. (AND ENSLAVED THE BRITONS!)

> I SAY, JOLLY NICE HERE, WHAT?

TRIBES LIKE THE **ANGLES** AND **JUTES** STARTED INVADING TOO. EVENTUALLY, THEY ALL MERGED INTO THE **ANGLO-SAXONS**.

ONCE THE ILLITERATE ANGLO-SAXONS TOOK OVER, PEOPLE **FORGOT** HOW TO **READ** AND **WRITE**! MONKS KEPT KNOWLEDGE ALIVE IN REMOTE IRISH MONASTERIES.

UNTIL **ME**! I HIRED THOSE MONKS TO TEACH MY SUBJECTS AND PUT BRITAIN BACK ON THE ROAD TO CIVILISATION!

ORIGINALLY PAGANS, THE ANGLO-SAXONS CONVERTED TO CHRISTIANITY TOO. IRONICALLY, THEY BECAME LIKE THEIR BRITON FOREBEARS: RIPE FOR **INVASION**, THIS TIME BY...

Vikings

RAIDING PARTIES FROM NORWAY AND DENMARK BEGAN BY ATTACKING MONASTERIES AND COASTAL TOWNS, AND SOON CONCLUDED BRITAIN WAS READY FOR A TAKEOVER!

THE BEST SHIP OF THE AGE, THE **VIKING LONGBOAT**, ALLOWED THEM TO STRIKE ANYWHERE ALONG THE COAST WITHOUT WARNING!

VIKINGS TRAVELLED AS FAR AS RUSSIA AND THE MIDDLE EAST. THEY EVEN MADE IT AS FAR AS **CANADA**!

DESPITE A BARBAROUS REPUTATION, THE VIKINGS WERE COMPARATIVELY HYGIENIC, BATHING ONCE A WEEK AND COMBING AND BRAIDING THEIR HAIR DAILY.

> PTH!

NOTE: "COMPARATIVELY HYGIENIC" — ISLAMIC OBSERVERS WERE **TOTALLY** GROSSED OUT BY THEIR HABIT OF **SPITTING** IN THEIR FACE-WASHING WATER BEFORE **PASSING IT TO SOMEONE ELSE**!

ROMANS LEAVE **400** AD, IRISH AND ANGLO-SAXONS INVADE: ~**450** AD.

> SEE YA.

ANGLO-SAXONS EXPAND, BRITONS RETREAT: ~**450-800** AD.

> HA! FEEL THE WEIGHT OF ANGLO-SAXON OPPRESSION!

> AW GEEZ.

VIKINGS CONQUER LARGE AREAS BEFORE MAKING PEACE WITH ALFRED IN **898** AD.

> HA! FEEL THE WEIGHT OF VIKING OPPRESSION!

> THIS SEEMS FAMILIAR...

| ROMANS | IRISH/PICTS | BRITONS | ANGLO-SAXONS | VIKINGS |

SO, EVERYONE KNOWS HISTORY'S MOST MEMORABLE DATE — **1066**, WHEN WILLIAM THE CONQUEROR, ER, **CONQUERED** ENGLAND! NOW, LET'S HEAR FROM THE **LOSING** SIDE.

PLEASE WELCOME THE GUY WHO WAS **NEARLY** ENGLAND'S MOST FAMOUS KING — IT'S...

HAROLD GODWINSON!

HAROLD GODWINSON
ENGLISH KING
c. 1022–1066

HAROLD, YOU GOT STOMPED ON BY WILLIAM AND HIS NORMANS AT THE BATTLE OF HASTINGS, BUT IT COULD'VE JUST AS EASILY GONE THE OTHER WAY...

LOL, I KNOW, RIGHT? IF THIS ARROW HAD GONE TWO FEET TO ONE SIDE, HISTORY MIGHT BE TOTALLY DIFFERENT!

IN FACT, YOUR **WHOLE STORY'S** A VERITABLE **WHIRLWIND** OF UNLUCKY COINCIDENCES. EVEN THE WAY YOU BECAME KING!

YEAH, I GUESS SO...

I WAS AN EARL, WHICH IS A SORT OF REGIONAL SUB-KING, BUT I WASN'T ACTUALLY RELATED TO THE ROYAL FAMILY AT ALL...*

THE KING, **EDWARD THE CONFESSOR**, SPENT ALL HIS TIME CONFESSING HIS SINS, SO I ENDED UP RUNNING THE COUNTRY FOR HIM.

...SO, ONE TIME I KICKED A KITTEN...

THAT ALSO MEANT HE WAS TOO BUSY TO HAVE ANY **CHILDREN**, SO THE THRONE WOULD BE LEFT EMPTY WHEN HE DIED...

...AND **ANOTHER** TIME I ATE ALL THE BISCUITS AND BLAMED IT ON MY BROTHER...

WHICH WAS A PROBLEM — YOU CAN'T HAVE A KINGDOM WITHOUT A KING! SO EDWARD CAME UP WITH A SOLUTION...

OK, DON'T WORRY GUYS — I GOT THIS...

YOU SEE, HE HAD SPENT HIS CHILDHOOD IN THE LAND OF THE **NORMANS**, SO HE WAS THEIR BIGGEST FAN!

NORMANS ARE COOL!

SO CLASSY...

SO HE NOMINATED **WILLIAM**, DUKE OF THE NORMANS, TO BE KING!

DID HE REALLY DO THAT!? I THOUGHT IT WAS JUST WILLIAM'S PROPAGANDA...

NO, NO — KING EDWARD EVEN MADE ME GO OVER TO FRANCE TO PROMISE WILLIAM I'D LET HIM BE KING.

I, HAROLD, DO SOLEMNLY SWEAR...

BUT WHAT WAS I SUPPOSED TO DO!? THE ENGLISH NOBLES ALL WANTED **ME** TO BE KING!

PLEEASE HAROLD!

WE CAN'T HAVE A NORMAN KING!

WE'D ALL HAVE TO LEARN **FRENCH**!

WAIT. I'M CONFUSED — IS WILLIAM **NORMAN** OR **FRENCH**?

WELL, BOTH...

THE NORMANS (OR **NORTH-MEN**) WERE BASICALLY JUST **VIKINGS** WHO'D SETTLED IN FRANCE, LEARNT FRENCH AND CUT THEIR HAIR.

ARR! L'ARR!

ANYWAY, I ROUNDED UP MY ARMY (MOST OF THEM WERE FARMERS, SO IT TOOK **AGES** TO COLLECT THEM ALL FROM THEIR FARMS) AND MARCHED DOWN TO THE SOUTH COAST. IF DUKE WILLIAM WANTED A FIGHT, HE COULD HAVE ONE...

*OK, HAROLD WAS MARRIED TO THE KING'S SISTER, BUT THAT WASN'T MUCH OF A CLAIM TO THE THRONE.

...ONLY WILLIAM DIDN'T SHOW UP! THE JERK WAS TOO BUSY "BUILDING SHIPS" AND "GATHERING HIS MEN" AND "WAITING FOR THE RIGHT WIND".

WELL, THAT'S GREAT, RIGHT? GAVE YOU TIME TO RELAX BEFORE THE BATTLE!

NO! **NOT** GREAT! I HAD TO GET ON WITH IT!

REMEMBER, MOST OF MY ARMY WERE ALSO **FARMERS**. THEY HAD TO GET HOME BEFORE HARVEST TIME, OR THE WHOLE COUNTRY WOULD STARVE!

IN THE END, I JUST COULD NOT WAIT ANY LONGER, AND I HAD TO LET THEM GO.

AND **THEN** THE NORMANS INVADED!?

ACTUALLY, THE WIND WAS STILL BLOWING SOUTH, SO NO, THEY COULDN'T SAIL. THEN **HARALD HARDRADA** INVADED...

HUH!? WHAT? WHO?

ONLY THE MOST FEARED **VIKING KING** FROM GREENLAND TO GREECE! HIS NAME BASICALLY MEANS "HARALD THE HARD-MAN", WHICH TELLS YOU ALL YOU NEED TO KNOW.

HIS **DAD'S FRIEND** HAD PROMISED HIM THE THRONE, OR SOMETHING, SO HE USED THE SOUTHERLY WINDS TO SNEAK IN BEFORE WILLIAM.

HEH HEH!

OI!

GEEZ. MY **AUNTIE'S CAT** ONCE MET THE QUEEN — CAN I CLAIM THE THRONE TOO?

I KNOW, RIGHT?

ANYWAY, RIDICULOUS CLAIM OR NOT, THESE VIKINGS WERE TAKING TOWNS ACROSS NORTHUMBERLAND...

WE THINK YOU'D BE A GREAT KING!

PLEASE DON'T KILL US!

WITH ONLY ONE THING FOR IT, I GATHERED UP WHAT WAS LEFT OF MY ARMY AND LEGGED IT NORTH!

COME ON, GUYS!

HUP! HUP! HUP!

WE MADE IT IN JUST **4 DAYS** — SO FAST, HARALD HARDRADA WAS COMPLETELY UNPREPARED...

DØN'T WØRRY! ENGLISH HÅRØLD IS **MILES** ÅWAY! HÅR HÅR...

IT WAS A **MASSACRE**! WE GAVE THOSE VIKINGS **SUCH A PASTING**, THEY NEVER TRIED TO INVADE ENGLAND AGAIN!

46

AND IF THAT'D BEEN THE END OF IT, YOU'D NOW BE REMEMBERED AS THE GUY WHO **SAVED ENGLAND** FROM THE VIKINGS...

BUT THAT **WASN'T** THE END OF IT. THE **WIND CHANGED**, SO WILLIAM COULD GET ACROSS THE CHANNEL.

OH, COME **ON**!

HEE HEE!

SO I GATHERED UP MY TROOPS AND LEGGED IT BACK SOUTH AGAIN...

COME ON, GUYS!

WE CAN DO THIS!

HUFF! PUFF!

EVEN THEN THE OUTCOME WASN'T GUARANTEED — THE ENGLISH AXE-MEN PERFORMED SURPRISINGLY WELL AGAINST THE NORMAN KNIGHTS, EVEN PUTTING THEM TO FLIGHT AT ONE POINT...

BUT IN THE END, IT ALL CAME DOWN TO THAT STRAY ARROW...

OW!

WITH NO KING TO RALLY AROUND, THE ENGLISH SOON GAVE IN...

FRENCH FOR BEGINNERS

SO IF EDWARD HADN'T DIED OR HARALD THE HARD-MAN HAD BEEN BUSY OR THE WINDS HAD CHANGED SOONER OR THE ARROW HAD MISSED, ALL OF HISTORY COULD'VE BEEN **RADICALLY DIFFERENT**!

AND IN THAT ALTERNATE HISTORY, PEOPLE WOULD THINK I'M COOL...?

I THINK YOU'RE COOL, HAROLD...

47

...AND MAKE THEM INTO SHIPS.
SHIPS OF REVENGE.

AND THE FIRST THING THEY DO IS STEAL
SOME POOR PEASANTS' COWS.

THEY HAVE A MASSIVE BARBEQUE.
CAN'T GO FIGHTING INJUSTICE ON
AN EMPTY STOMACH...

LET IT GO, DAD. IT'S JUST A COW...

WILLIAM GIVES A ROUSING SPEECH.

THE NORMANS BEGIN THEIR CAVALRY CHARGE.

OK, BOYS.

LET'S KICK THEIR BUTTS.

THEY SMASH UP AGAINST THE ENGLISH SHIELD-WALL.

HORSES ARE DYING LEFT AND RIGHT.

THE ENGLISH ARE ON TOP OF A HILL, AND FOR
A WHILE IT LOOKS LIKE THEY MIGHT WIN...

THEY CROSS THE HECK OVER THE ENGLISH CHANNEL.

WOO!

YEAH!

KEBAB?

DON'T MIND IF I DO...

NOM NOM NOM.

WELL, THIS IS JOLLY NICE.

THEN WILLIAM HEARS THAT HAROLD IS ON HIS WAY.

IMAGINE SOME DRAMATIC MUSIC HERE...

THE FIGHTING GETS TOTALLY CRAZY.

EVERYONE'S HACKING AT EVERYONE ELSE.

A RUMOUR STARTS THAT WILLIAM'S BEEN KILLED...

LOOK! HE'S FINE!

I'M FINE!

BUT THEN HAROLD GETS IT IN THE EYE — IT'S ALL OVER.

AAGH!

AND NOW, IT'S THE **BAD TEMPER** THAT TORE ENGLAND IN **TWO!** THAT'S RIGHT, MY GUEST IS THE **FIRST** RULING QUEEN OF ENGLAND...

THE EASILY ANGERED ANCESTOR OF THE ANGEVIN EMPIRE...

EMPRESS MATILDA! (OR MAUD!)

EMPRESS MATILDA
ENGLISH QUEEN
1102–1167

ACTUALLY, MATILDA OR MAUD - WHICH ONE IS IT?

IT'S THE SAME NAME. IT MEANS "MIGHTY IN BATTLE", WHICH I FIND RATHER APROPOS...

MATILDA IS THE LATIN VERSION, SO THAT'S WHAT KINGS AND NOBLES CALLED ME. WELL, ACTUALLY THEY CALLED ME "YOUR HIGHNESS", BUT YOU KNOW WHAT I MEAN...

MAUD IS JUST THE SAXON VERSION OF THE NAME. THAT'S WHAT MY PEASANTS AND SERFS CALLED ME. ACTUALLY, MAYBE **YOU'D** BETTER USE THAT...

So anyway, **Matilda**, you were sent by your father, **Henry I**, to marry the Holy Roman Emperor, **Henry V**, when you were just **8 years old**.

Must've been pretty rough, having to leave your family and go to a strange place where you didn't even speak the language.

Oh, I liked it!

I had tutors to teach me German and how to act like an empress.

The wave has more of a **twisting** motion. Imagine you're balancing an egg...

Plus, I was the first lady of Europe's most **powerful** empire! I was loved and respected, and **everyone** had to do what I said.

But all that changed almost overnight when my brother, **William**, died in the **White Ship disaster**.

He'd got **stinking drunk**, along with the entire crew, and thought it would be hilarious if they could overtake our father's ship, when he hit a rock. Sort of a medieval **joyriding accident**.

Fashter!
≈ hic ≈
Fashter!

So now I was heir to the throne. And then my husband, Henry, died and my dad, Henry, summoned me back to Normandy.

So confusing...

Which I was **not** pleased about! I was quite happy in the heart of European civilisation. I didn't want to rule a bunch of backwoods bumpkins!

But Henry (dad) insisted, and made all his nobles swear to accept me as their ruler when he died.

Needless to say, a bunch of medieval warlords were not best pleased at the thought of a female ruler...

HUBBA RUBBA RUBBA RUBBA

BUT EVEN **THAT** MIGHT NOT HAVE BEEN A PROBLEM, EXCEPT DAD DIED SUDDENLY FROM EATING TOO MANY **LAMPREYS**.

I THINK I'D DIE IF I ATE EVEN **ONE** OF THESE HORRIBLE THINGS.

THEY'RE A DELICACY. ANYWAY, THE POINT IS, I WAS NOT IN ENGLAND AT THIS TIME.

SO MY ROTTEN COUSIN **STEPHEN** GOT THERE FIRST!

NYEH! NYEH!

YOU SNOOZE, YOU LOSE!

HE WAS ONE OF THE NOBLEMEN WHO'D ALREADY SWORN TO ACCEPT ME AS QUEEN, SO HE WAS TOTALLY **BREAKING HIS PROMISE**...

JUST COULDN'T HANDLE BEING TOLD WHAT TO DO BY A **WOMAN**!

RIGHT, BUT STEPHEN ARGUED THAT IT WAS **INEVITABLE** THAT THE BARONS WOULD REBEL AGAINST A WOMAN LEADER ANYWAY, SO HE WAS REALLY JUST TRYING TO KEEP THE PEACE.

AND FOR A WHILE THERE, IT LOOKED LIKE HE MIGHT ACTUALLY BE A PRETTY GOOD KING! PEOPLE LIKED HIM, HE WAS FRIENDLY AND GENEROUS.

HEY! I'M JUST SAYIN'...

PFF! STEPHEN WAS TOO **WEAK** TO BE KING! HE RELIED TOO MUCH ON HIS SUPPORTERS' GOOD WILL, SO HE HAD TO KEEP GIVING THEM MONEY AND LAND. SOON HE RAN OUT OF BOTH.

WHEREAS **I** NEVER BOTHERED TRYING TO KEEP PEOPLE HAPPY. I'M AN **EMPRESS!** IT WAS EVERYONE **ELSE'S** JOB TO KEEP **ME** HAPPY, NOT THE OTHER WAY AROUND!

BUT **THAT** WAS **EXACTLY** YOUR PROBLEM. FOR EXAMPLE, YOU WERE SO **RUDE** TO THE PEOPLE OF LONDON, THEY SHUT YOU OUT OF THE CITY!

AND WHEN YOUR UNCLE, THE KING OF SCOTLAND, SUGGESTED YOU SPEAK MORE NICELY TO PEOPLE, YOU PUNCHED HIM IN THE **HEAD**!

GYAAH! THIS IS MY POINT! IF EVERYONE HAD JUST DONE WHAT I TOLD THEM, **WHEN** I TOLD THEM, EVERYTHING WOULD'VE BEEN FINE!

BUT INSTEAD, YOUR **SUCCESSION SQUABBLE** PLUNGED ENGLAND INTO TWENTY YEARS OF CIVIL WAR, LAWLESSNESS AND DESTRUCTION, KNOWN AS **THE ANARCHY.**

AT ONE POINT YOU EVEN CAPTURED STEPHEN AND PUT HIM IN PRISON, BUT THEN YOU LET HIM GO. WHICH SEEMS LIKE A PRETTY DUMB MOVE, IF I'M TOTALLY HONEST.

I HAD NO **CHOICE!** HIS SUPPORTERS CAPTURED MY HALF-BROTHER ROBERT, WHO WAS THE ONLY GUY WHO ACTUALLY DID AS HE WAS TOLD! I **NEEDED** THAT GUY – SO WE DID A SWAP.

I ALMOST GOT CAPTURED MYSELF; I ONLY ESCAPED BY HAVING MYSELF CARRIED OUT IN A **COFFIN!**

KEEP AN EYE OUT FOR MATILDA.

OR MAUD...

IN FACT, YOU BECAME QUITE THE ESCAPE ARTIST! YOU ALSO ESCAPED FROM THE WINTER SIEGE OF OXFORD CASTLE, BY CAMOUFLAGING YOURSELF ALL IN WHITE AND RUNNING ACROSS THE FROZEN THAMES!

BUT IN THE END, IT BECAME A **STALEMATE.** NEITHER OF YOU COULD EVER WIN, SO YOU AGREED ON A **COMPROMISE.**

RIGHT. STUPID **STEPHEN** GOT TO STAY KING, BUT HE PROMISED THAT **MY** SON HENRY WOULD INHERIT THE THRONE AFTER HIS DEATH.

SO MANY **HENRYS...**

THIS ONE WAS **HENRY II,** WHO'S **ALSO** FAMOUS FOR HIS AMAZINGLY BAD TEMPER.

YOU BETTER NOT BE TALKIN' TRASH ABOUT MY SON...

YOU'RE NOT DOING YOURSELF ANY FAVOURS HERE...

THE OLD BAILEY

THE **ANARCHY**, THE CHAOTIC CIVIL WAR BETWEEN THE EMPRESS MATILDA AND HER ROYAL RIVAL, KING STEPHEN, SAW A SUDDEN RASH OF **CASTLE-BUILDING**.

BAH! CASTLES WERE **SUPPOSED** TO BE BUILT ONLY WITH **ROYAL PERMISSION**, BUT **STUPID STEPHEN** COUDN'T CONTROL HIS BARONS, SO ILLEGAL CASTLES STARTED POPPING UP ALL OVER THE PLACE.

ONCE THEY HAD AN IMPREGNABLE FORTRESS TO HIDE OUT IN, THEY COULD GET AWAY WITH MURDER.

LITERALLY, THERE WERE ROBBER BARONS ROAMING THE COUNTRYSIDE, KILLING AND STEALING AT WILL.

THE MOTTE-AND-BAILEY CASTLE WAS A PARTICULAR PROBLEM, SINCE A HIGHLY MOTIVATED ROBBER BARON COULD GET A SIMPLE ONE BUILT IN A **WEEK**!

THE **BAILEY**, OR LOWER COURTYARD, HOUSED THE BUILDINGS THAT KEPT THE BARON'S WAR-MACHINE RUNNING.

STOREHOUSES

STABLES

A **GATEHOUSE** AND **DRAWBRIDGE** CONTROLLED WHO COULD GET IN AND OUT.

BAKERY

WATER WELL

ARMOURY

BLACKSMITH

A **PALISADE**, A FENCE OF GIANT LOGS WITH A RAISED WALKWAY FOR DEFENDERS, SURROUNDED THE CASTLE. IT MIGHT BE REINFORCED WITH **GARILLUM**, RUBBLE PACKED BETWEEN THE INNER AND OUTER WALLS.

THE **FOSSE**, A LONG DITCH, SURROUNDED BOTH COMPOUNDS. THIS WOULD OFTEN BE FLOODED TO MAKE A **MOAT** BY DIVERTING A NEARBY STREAM.

MEET THE KURDISH COMMANDER WHO **OUT-CRUSADED** THE **CRUSADERS**, WHILE CONCURRENTLY **CONFOUNDING** THEM WITH **CHIVALRY**!

PLEASE WELCOME THE **NICE GUY** OF THE **NEAR EAST**. IT'S SALAH AD-DIN YUSUF IBN AYYUB, OR AS HE'S BETTER KNOWN HERE IN THE WEST...

SALADIN!

SALADIN
SULTAN OF EGYPT AND SYRIA
1137–1193

SALADIN, YOU BECAME FAMOUS AMONG MEDIEVAL CHRISTIANS FOR YOUR HONOUR, FAIRNESS AND DECENCY, DESPITE THE FACT THAT YOU'D JUST KICKED THEM OUT OF THE HOLY CITY OF JERUSALEM.

THAT'S GOTTA BE PRETTY RARE – A CONQUEROR BEING BIGGED-UP BY THE VERY PEOPLE HE'S JUST **BEATEN**?

WELL, THE **QUR'AN** TEACHES US TO ANSWER EVIL WITH GOOD, AND SO TURN OUR ENEMIES INTO FRIENDS.

BUT WHY WERE YOU ENEMIES IN THE FIRST PLACE? I MEAN, THE CRUSADERS WERE KNIGHTS FROM EUROPE, RIGHT? WHAT WERE THEY DOING ALL THE WAY OVER THERE?

WELL, IT ALL BEGAN IN THE TIME OF OUR GREAT-GRANDFATHERS...

 THE CHRISTIAN BYZANTINE EMPIRE HAD BEEN INVADED BY MUSLIM TURKS, AND SO THE EMPEROR ASKED THE POPE TO SEND HELP.

EUROPE

BYZANTINE EMPIRE

TURKS

 BUT HE GOT MORE THAN HE BARGAINED FOR WHEN A CRUSADER ARMY TURNED UP, INTENT ON RETAKING NOT ONLY **HIS** LANDS, BUT ALSO JERUSALEM FOR THEMSELVES.

TO JERUSALEM

WHEN THEY FINALLY TOOK JERUSALEM, THEY PUT THE WHOLE CITY TO THE SWORD. MEN, WOMEN AND CHILDREN, MUSLIM, JEW AND CHRISTIAN ALIKE, UNTIL THE STREETS **RAN** WITH BLOOD.

 NOT REALLY, ER... VERY CHRISTIAN OF THEM...

MY THOUGHTS EXACTLY.

 NOW IN FAIRNESS, BY **MY** TIME, THE DESCENDANTS OF THOSE FIRST CRUSADERS HAD **MELLOWED** A BIT...

 THEY'D BEEN LIVING HERE, FIGHTING A BIT, BUT ALSO TRADING AND EVEN MAKING FRIENDS WITH THE LOCALS.

 THE **REAL** PROBLEM WAS THAT FRESH CRUSADERS KEPT **SHOWING UP**, MOSTLY PENNILESS KNIGHTS KEEN TO MAKE THEIR FORTUNES BY KILLING THE LOCALS AND STEALING THEIR STUFF!

GUYS LIKE **RAYNALD OF CHATILLON**.

UGH. **THAT** GUY...

 I HAD MANAGED TO NEGOTIATE A TRUCE, BUT RAYNALD KEPT BREAKING IT: ATTACKING MERCHANTS WHO WERE UNDER MY PROTECTION.

DIE, INFIDEL!

AAH!

ONE TIME, HE EVEN CARRIED A FLEET OF SHIPS **ACROSS THE DESERT** TO TRY AND ATTACK THE MOST HOLY PLACES OF ISLAM.

I MEAN, COME **ON**! WHO **DOES** THAT!?

BUT ISN'T IT RIGHT THAT YOU COULDN'T STOP HIM BECAUSE YOU WERE BUSY FIGHTING OTHER MUSLIMS?

YEAH, I HEARD THAT A LOT...

BUT LOOK: HERE'S THE THING. WE **NEEDED** A RULER. WE GOT BEATEN BECAUSE WE WERE TOO BUSY FIGHTING AMONGST OURSELVES.

IT'S NOT LIKE I **WANTED** IT TO BE ME — I WAS MUCH HAPPIER AS A NOBODY. MORE TIME FOR **READING**...

BUT THEN ONE DAY MY UNCLE, WHO WAS A GENERAL FOR THE SULTAN OF SYRIA, BURST INTO MY ROOM.

YUSUF! PACK YOUR BAGS — WE'RE INVADING EGYPT!

EGYPT? BUT JERUSALEM'S NOT IN EGYPT?

WE'RE COMING TO IT. THIS IS A FLASHBACK SEQUENCE...

YOU SEE, EGYPT'S NILE VALLEY WAS THE ONLY REALLY RICH **FARMLAND** IN THE AREA, SO THE CRUSADERS WERE ALWAYS **ITCHING** TO GET THEIR HANDS ON IT.

SO MY UNCLE INVADED TO MAKE SURE THAT DIDN'T HAPPEN, AND I GOT DRAGGED ALONG FOR THE RIDE...

WAH?

HE FOUGHT OFF THE CRUSADERS, TOOK OVER THE COUNTRY AND THEN CONVENIENTLY **DIED**, LEAVING ME IN CHARGE.

THEN OUR OLD BOSS, THE SULTAN OF SYRIA, DIED LEAVING HIS TEENAGED SON IN CHARGE, WHO **ALSO** DIED...

SO I FIGURED: OK, MAYBE GOD **WANTS** ME TO TAKE OVER.

OH, YEAH? NEVER HEARD **THAT** ONE BEFORE...

NO, BUT COME ON — IT'S A PRETTY FREAKY CHAIN OF COINCIDENCES, YOU GOTTA ADMIT!

STILL NOT PROOF OF THE DIVINE WILL.

60

OK, FINE. THE POINT IS: PEOPLE BELIEVED IT! PLUS, THIS **RAYNALD** CHARACTER WAS MAKING EVERYONE SO **MAD**, THEY UNITED UNDER MY BANNER JUST SO THEY COULD TEACH HIM A LESSON!

FORTUNATELY FOR ME, THE CRUSADERS HAD A NEW KING, A GUY CALLED **GUY**, WHO WAS ANOTHER OF THOSE RECENT EUROPEAN IMPORTS, AND A TOTAL **MUPPET!**

HUR HUR! I'M THE KING!

HE ALLOWED ME TO LURE HIM OUT INTO THE DESERT WITHOUT ANY WATER! DRIVEN MAD WITH HEAT AND THIRST, HIS KNIGHTS WERE EASY PICKINGS!

I IMPRISONED KING GUY, EXECUTED RAYNALD AND THE WORST OF THE TROUBLE-MAKERS, AND SOLD EVERYONE ELSE AS SLAVES.

THERE WERE **SO MANY** OF THEM, THE PRICE OF SLAVES CRASHED. PEOPLE WERE BEING SWAPPED FOR **SHOES.**

OH, COME ON! I'M WORTH A PAIR OF HI-TOPS AT LEAST!

PLUS, SINCE GUY HAD MADE THE SCHOOLBOY ERROR OF COMMITTING HIS **ENTIRE ARMY** TO ONE BATTLE, THERE WAS ALMOST NO ONE LEFT TO DEFEND JERUSALEM.

HELLOOO?

BUT IN CONTRAST TO THE CHRISTIANS' ORIGINAL CONQUEST, YOUR TAKEOVER WAS ALMOST ENTIRELY **BLOODLESS.**

NOT ONLY WERE THE FEW DEFENDERS UNHARMED, BUT ANY CITIZENS WHO WANTED TO COULD LEAVE, TAKING THEIR STUFF WITH THEM.

YOU ALLOWED CHRISTIANS FREE ACCESS TO THE CITY FOR PILGRIMAGE, EVEN SETTING UP A SPECIAL GUARD TO ENSURE THEIR SAFETY.

THIS WAY, SIR...

WORD OF YOUR FAIRNESS SPREAD THROUGHOUT THE CHRISTIAN WEST...

THIS INFIDEL IS GIVING US A LESSON IN THE TRUE MEANING OF **CHIVALRY...**

SO TRUE...

NODS

SPARKING ANOTHER CRUSADE.

LET'S GO KICK HIS BUTT!

YEAH!

-SIGH- I GUESS SOME THINGS NEVER CHANGE...

GIFTS OF GENIUS

SALADIN, THE LION OF ISLAM, WHO KILLED THE CRUSADERS WITH **KINDNESS** (AND WITH, Y'KNOW, ACTUAL KILLING) IS BACK TO SHARE SOME OF THE AMAZING STUFF WE ALL OWE TO THE MEDIEVAL ISLAMIC WORLD!

THAT'S RIGHT! THE CRUSADES WEREN'T ALL ABOUT VIOLENT RELIGIOUS HATRED, OH NO, SIREE! FROM **SPAIN** TO **SAMARKAND**, ISLAMIC INNOVATORS WERE MAKING A DAZZLING ARRAY OF DISCOVERIES, WHICH MADE THEIR WAY BACK TO THE CHRISTIAN WEST, AND WHICH YOU MODERN FOLKS STILL USE EVERY DAY...

MEDICINE

MUSLIM, CHRISTIAN AND JEWISH DOCTORS WORKING IN THE EAST WERE FAR MORE ADVANCED THAN THEIR WESTERN COUNTERPARTS, WITH AN UNDERSTANDING OF THINGS LIKE BLOOD CIRCULATION THAT WOULDN'T BE MATCHED IN THE WEST FOR CENTURIES.

I ONCE LENT MY PERSONAL DOCTOR TO **RICHARD THE LIONHEART**. EVEN THOUGH WE WERE ENEMIES, I COULDN'T STAND SEEING WHAT HIS **OWN** DOCTOR WAS DOING TO HIM!

NUMBERS

THE DECIMAL SYSTEM OF NUMBERS FROM 0 TO 9 WAS INVENTED IN INDIA, AND QUICKLY SPREAD THROUGHOUT THE ISLAMIC WORLD.

ITALIAN MATHEMATICIAN **LEONARDO FIBONACCI** LEARNED ABOUT THEM WHILE STUDYING IN MUSLIM NORTH AFRICA, AND REALISED WHAT AN IMPROVEMENT THEY'D BE ON THE OLD ROMAN IXVC-TYPE NUMERALS.

I'VE GOT TO TELL EVERYONE ABOUT THIS!

SH!

FOODS

JUST SOME OF THE FRUITS AND VEGETABLES THE MUSLIM WORLD INTRODUCED TO EUROPE, WITH THEIR ORIGINAL ARABIC NAMES:

AL-BARQUQ (APRICOT)

AL-KHARSHUF (ARTICHOKE)

AL-BADINJAN (AUBERGINE)

LIMUN (LEMON)

NARANJ (ORANGE)

ISBINAKH (SPINACH)

SADLY, IT SEEMS TO HAVE TAKEN PEOPLE A WHILE TO LEARN HOW TO **USE** THEM. THE EUROPEAN TAKEAWAY AREA IN JERUSALEM WAS KNOWN LOCALLY AS THE **STREET OF BAD COOKING.**

THE EARLY MUSLIMS BEGAN A MAJOR PROJECT TO TRANSLATE AND BUILD ON THE WORKS OF THE ANCIENT SCHOLARS, ESPECIALLY THE FAMOUS ANCIENT GREEKS.

SO MUCH OF THE KNOWLEDGE THAT WAS **LOST** IN EUROPE AFTER THE ROMAN EMPIRE COLLAPSED WAS **PRESERVED** IN THE EAST.

ALSO, THEIR VAST TRADING NETWORKS ALLOWED PEOPLE AND GOODS TO TRAVEL FROM INDIA AND CHINA, MAKING IT EASIER TO SPREAD INNOVATIONS.

OOH! THAT'S A GOOD IDEA...

COTTON FROM THE ARABIC: QUTN

LIGHT, STRONG AND **WAY** LESS ITCHY THAN WOOL, COTTON COULD BE WOVEN INTO ALL SORTS OF FINE FABRICS NEVER BEFORE SEEN IN EUROPE.

COMBINED WITH NEW DYES, LIKE CRIMSON (FROM THE ARABIC **QIRMIZI**), IT LED TO A **REVOLUTION** IN MEDIEVAL FASHION.

NICE SHOES.

CHESS FROM THE PERSIAN: SHAH, MEANING KING.

ANOTHER INDIAN INVENTION THAT SPREAD THROUGH THE ISLAMIC WORLD TO EUROPE.

ALONG THE WAY, SOME OF THE PIECES WERE ADAPTED TO MAKE MORE SENSE TO EUROPEANS. SO **VIZIER** BECAME **QUEEN**, **ELEPHANT** BECAME **BISHOP** AND **CHARIOT** (**RUKH** IN PERSIAN) BECAME **ROOK**.

CHECKMATE!

SUGAR FROM THE ARABIC: SUKKAR.

YEP, THAT'S RIGHT! BEFORE THE CRUSADES, THE ONLY SOURCE OF SWEETNESS IN EUROPE WAS HONEY, SO WHEN THEY GOT A TASTE OF **SUGAR**, THE WEST WENT WILD FOR IT!

UH, APOLOGIES TO ANY **DENTISTS** OUT THERE...

PAPER

INVENTED IN CHINA AND REFINED AND INDUSTRIALISED IN BAGHDAD, **PAPER** MADE BOOKS LIGHTER, STRONGER AND MUCH, MUCH CHEAPER THAN THE ANIMAL-SKIN **PARCHMENT** BEING USED IN THE WEST.

ULTIMATELY ALLOWING YOU TO READ **THIS** BOOK! HEY, YOU'RE WELCOME!

MY NEXT GUEST IS ONE OF ENGLAND'S MOST BELOVED MONARCHS. YOU MAY HAVE HEARD TALES OF HIS EXPLOITS ALONGSIDE THE LIKES OF **ROBIN HOOD**!

TO THIS DAY, HIS NAME IS A **WATCHWORD** FOR COURAGE, HONOUR AND CHIVALRY. IT'S...

RICHARD THE LIONHEART!

RICHARD THE LIONHEART

ENGLISH KING 1157–1199

WHICH IS IRONIC, BECAUSE HE'S ACTUALLY AS BIG A BULLY, SNEAK AND SPOILED BRAT AS YOU COULD EVER WISH **NOT** TO MEET!

WHA!

BUT... BUT... I AM THE GREAT HERO KING OF ENGLAND!

WELL, LET'S LOOK AT THE **FACTS**, SHALL WE?

YOU WERE HARDLY EVER EVEN IN ENGLAND, PREFERRING YOUR LANDS IN FRANCE.

WELL, COME ON! ENGLAND IS A **DUMP**! ALWAYS COLD AND RAINING!

YOU BECAME ONE OF THE GREATEST WARRIORS OF ALL TIME...

YEAH! THAT'S MORE LIKE IT!

IN PARTICULAR, YOU BECAME THE MASTER OF USING **SIEGE ENGINES** TO DESTROY THE CASTLES OF YOUR ENEMIES.

BATTERING RAM

CATAPULT

TREBUCHET

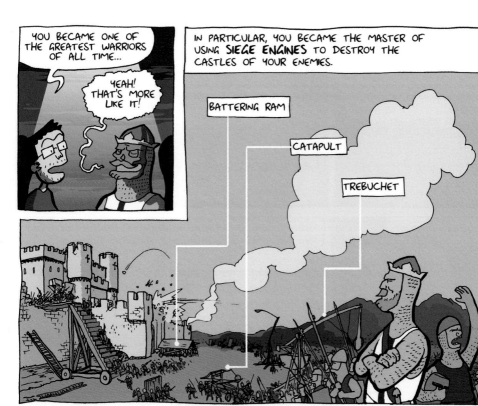

ESPECIALLY WHEN THE ENEMY WAS YOUR **OWN FATHER!**

WHAT ARE YOU **DOING!?**

DAD, YOU'RE GOING **DOWN.**

HE DIED OF **STRESS**, CAUSED BY **YOU!**

HEY! HE WANTED ME TO **SHARE** THE KINGDOM WITH MY LITTLE BROTHER JOHN. **NO WAY!**

THEN, AS SOON AS YOU BECAME KING, YOU LEFT TO JOIN THE **THIRD CRUSADE.** WHAT WAS **THAT** ALL ABOUT?

THE CRUSADER KINGDOM IN JERUSALEM HAD BEEN CONQUERED BY THE MUSLIMS. I WAS DETERMINED TO TAKE IT BACK!

SO I...

WAIT, WAIT... **WHY?** YOU HAD YOUR OWN KINGDOM. WHY BOTHER WITH WHAT HAPPENED HALF-WAY AROUND THE WORLD?

WELL, LOOK. I'D JUST KILLED MY OWN **DAD**, SO I WAS PRETTY SURE I WAS GOING TO **HELL**. ANYONE WHO TOOK PART IN THE CRUSADES WAS GIVEN A **GUARANTEED** TICKET **STRAIGHT TO HEAVEN!**

SO YOU PLANNED TO GET TO HEAVEN BY KILLING **MORE PEOPLE?** GENIUS.

HEY, IT'S NOT LIKE I WAS ABOUT TO START **DOING GOOD**, OR SOMETHING.

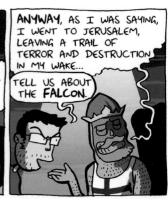

ANYWAY, AS I WAS SAYING, I WENT TO JERUSALEM, LEAVING A TRAIL OF TERROR AND DESTRUCTION IN MY WAKE...

TELL US ABOUT THE **FALCON**.

THE UH...

DO I HAVE TO?

-SIGH- I WAS OUT RIDING ONE DAY WHEN I SAW A PARTICULARLY FINE FALCON IN A POOR MAN'S HUT.

THAT'S **MUCH** TOO FINE A BIRD TO BELONG TO A MERE **PEASANT**...

REALLY, IT'S MY **DUTY**, AS A KING, TO **STEAL** IT...

WHACK!

YOU WERE SET UPON, BEATEN AND KICKED OUT OF THE VILLAGE BY A CROWD OF ANGRY PEASANTS!

ALL RIGHT, ALL RIGHT. LET'S GET ON TO MY GLORIOUS VICTORIES, SHALL WE?

YOU MEAN LIKE WHEN YOU RECONQUERED JERUSALEM? OH WAIT. THAT'S RIGHT. YOU **DIDN'T!**

OK, SERIOUSLY, CAN I GET ANOTHER INTERVIEWER?

YOU QUARRELLED WITH YOUR ALLIES, SO THEY ALL LEFT, TAKING THEIR ARMIES WITH THEM.

THEY WERE ALL **IDIOTS!** THEY DIDN'T UNDERSTAND MILITARY STRATEGY!

WE HAD JUST ONE CITY. WE NEEDED TO BUILD MORE CASTLES AND BE READY FOR A LONG WAR, BUT THEY JUST WANTED TO ATTACK JERUSALEM AND GO HOME.

ACRE
HAIFA
ARSUF
JAFFA
JERUSALEM
ASCALON

PLUS, I HEARD MY LITTLE BROTHER JOHN WAS PLOTTING TO TAKE OVER MY KINGDOM.

SO YOU GAVE UP.

I MADE A **TACTICAL WITHDRAWAL!**

TO GET HOME, I HAD TO PASS THROUGH THE LANDS OF MY ENEMIES, SO I DISGUISED MYSELF AS A **RETURNING PILGRIM.**

SO... HOW DO I LOOK?

VERY GOOD, SIRE.

PEASANTY.

BUT YOU WERE RECOGNISED BECAUSE YOU INSISTED ON EATING EXPENSIVE FOOD!

WHAT WAS IT AGAIN?

...ROAST CHICKEN...

...IT'S MY FAVOURITE.

YOU WERE IMPRISONED, AND YOUR SUBJECTS HAD TO PAY A **KING'S RANSOM** TO GET YOU OUT!

BAH!

YOUR BROTHER JOHN TRIED TO PAY THEM TO **KEEP** YOU IN PRISON!

BUT BEFORE LONG, YOU WERE BACK HOME, AND BACK TO YOUR OLD WAYS, BEATING AND CHEATING ANYONE WHO EVEN LOOKED AT YOU FUNNY!

OK YOU KNOW WHAT? I'M OUTTA HERE.

MEET ONE OF HISTORY'S MOST **FASCINATING** AND **ELUSIVE** FIGURES! HE'S THE **BLOODSTAINED BARBARIAN** WHO BUILT A **BUREAUCRACY OF BUTCHERY,** BUT LOST IT ALL TO A HANDFUL OF CONQUISTADOR CHANCERS!

IT'S THE LAST FREE EMPEROR OF THE AZTECS...

MOCTEZUMA **II**!

MOCTEZUMA II

AZTEC EMPEROR

C. 1466–1520

MOCTEZUMA, YOU AZTECS ARE FAMOUS FOR YOUR BLOODY RITUALS OF **HUMAN SACRIFICE,** TEARING OUT THE **HEARTS** OF YOUR VICTIMS TO APPEASE YOUR BLOODTHIRSTY DEITIES!

OH, **COME ON!** WHY DOES EVERYONE ALWAYS FOCUS ON THAT!?

THERE'S **WAY** MORE TO THE AZTECS THAN **RITUAL MURDER:** WE HAD A REFINED AND SOPHISTICATED CIVILISATION...

TENOCHTITLAN, OUR CAPITAL CITY, WITH ITS BEAUTIFUL STREETS, CANALS AND TEMPLES BUILT RIGHT OUT ONTO THE LAKE, WAS THE WONDER OF THE NEW WORLD!

WHILE ALL AROUND IT, LUSH FLOATING GARDENS GREW FOOD AND THE AZTECS' GREAT LOVE: **FLOWERS!**

PLUS WE HAD ADVANCED MATHEMATICS, A HIGHLY DEVELOPED PICTURE WRITING SYSTEM, UNIVERSAL EDUCATION...

BUT YOU STILL **SACRIFICED** PEOPLE, RIGHT?

OH, YEAH. **THOUSANDS** OF 'EM.

BUT WE **HAD** TO! AFTER ALL – THE GODS EXPEND THEIR OWN **LIFE ENERGY** KEEPING THE SUN IN THE SKY, THE RAIN FALLING AND **TIME ITSELF** MOVING...

IF WE AZTECS DIDN'T KEEP THEM FED WITH LIFE ENERGY (IN THE FORM OF STILL-BEATING HUMAN HEARTS) THEY MIGHT JUST... **STOP.**

THAT'S... A WEIRD THEORY. HOW COULD YOU BE SO SURE IT WAS **TRUE?**

DUDE! **TIME** MIGHT **STOP!** DO YOU **REALLY** WANNA TAKE THAT CHANCE!?

PLUS, THE **MORE** WE FED THEM WITH SACRIFICES, THE MORE THE GODS FAVOURED US...

THE AZTEC RECORD WAS **80,400** IN **4** DAYS AT THE RE-DEDICATION OF THE GREAT TEMPLE AT TENOCHTITLAN.

MY ARM'S GETTING TIRED!

I KNOW! IT'S MURDER!

AND IT WORKED, AT LEAST FOR A WHILE. WE BUILT A HUGE EMPIRE ON **FEAR,** TAKING CARE TO LEAVE SOME PEOPLE UNCONQUERED SO WE COULD KEEP FIGHTING THEM TO CAPTURE MORE SACRIFICES.

UNTIL THE SPANISH ARRIVED.

-GROAN- DON'T REMIND ME!

WELL, YOU KNEW WE HAD TO GET TO IT EVENTUALLY! IT'S ONE OF THE GREAT EVENTS IN HISTORY; YOUR **FIRST CONTACT** WITH EUROPEAN EXPLORERS!

WELL, IT WASN'T THAT GREAT FOR **ME**! THESE WEIRD GUYS JUST SHOWED UP ONE DAY AND STARTED TEARING MY WORLD APART!

I USED **LONG-DISTANCE RUNNERS** TO GATHER NEWS FROM THE DISTANT PROVINCES OF THE EMPIRE, AND THE NEWS ON THESE STRANGERS WAS **TERRIFYING...**

I MEAN, THESE GUYS HAD FREAKIN' **SUPERPOWERS**! LIKE, THEY COULD SHOOT FIRE AND BLOW PEOPLE UP!

BUT WHEN **WE** SHOT AT THEM, THE ARROWS JUST BOUNCED OFF!

AND THEY WERE LED BY GUYS RIDING ON GIGANTIC, MONSTROUS **BEASTS**!

I THINK THOSE ARE CALLED **HORSES...**

I KNOW THAT **NOW**! BUT REMEMBER, NO ONE IN AMERICA HAD EVEN **HEARD** OF A HORSE BEFORE! (THAT'S WHY WE USED RUNNERS.)

AND THEN, TO TOP IT ALL OFF, THEY MADE AN ALLIANCE WITH THE **TLAXCALANS.**

THE **WHO**?

REMEMBER WE LEFT SOME GUYS **UNCONQUERED** SO WE COULD KEEP CAPTURING THEM FOR HUMAN SACRIFICES? **THOSE** GUYS.

SO NOW A **MASSIVE** ARMY OF OUR **WORST ENEMIES**, LED BY A BUNCH OF **SUPER-HUMANS** ARE ALL MARCHING TOWARDS MY CAPITAL...

WHAT DID YOU DO?

WHAT DO YOU **THINK** I DID!? I SAID: "OH, HOW NICE TO SEE YOU. COME ON IN. PLEASE DON'T DESTROY MY NICE CITY..."

HOW WAS **I** TO KNOW THEY WERE GOING TO **KIDNAP** ME AND TAKE OVER!?

SO HOLD ON — YOU'RE A PRISONER IN YOUR **OWN PALACE,** SURROUNDED BY **THOUSANDS** OF FANATICAL WARRIORS READY TO **DIE** AT YOUR BIDDING...

WHY NOT JUST COMMAND THEM TO ATTACK?

AND GET **KILLED** IN THE PROCESS!? OH, THANKS **VERY** MUCH!

SO YOU CONDEMNED THOUSANDS TO DIE BENEATH THE SACRIFICIAL KNIFE, BUT WHEN IT CAME TO IT, YOU LET THE SPANISH WIN TO SAVE YOUR OWN SKIN.

HEY, YOU WEREN'T **THERE,** MAN!

THESE GUYS WERE LIKE NOTHING ON EARTH! THEY DIDN'T WORSHIP THE GODS! THEY DIDN'T PERFORM SACRIFICES! AND YET THE GODS FAVOURED THEM WITH VICTORY!

SO I FIGURED THAT THE BEST THING WAS TO PLAY NICE, STALL FOR TIME AND MAYBE LEARN THEIR WEAKNESSES.

BUT AN AZTEC LEADER IS ONLY RESPECTED FOR **DEFEATING** HIS ENEMIES, NOT FOR PLAYING NICE WITH THEM...

EVENTS RAN AWAY FROM YOU, AND WHEN THE AZTECS FINALLY ROSE UP IN REBELLION, YOU TRIED TO TALK THEM OUT OF IT...

DISGUSTED AT THEIR COWARDLY LEADER, YOUR **OWN PEOPLE** STONED YOU TO DEATH!

I GUESS YOU COULD SAY YOU GOT CAUGHT BETWEEN **SOME ROCKS** AND A HARD PLACE...

OK, OK. **FINE.** MOST OF THE AZTECS' VICTIMS WERE PRISONERS CAPTURED IN WAR. WE DEVELOPED A SYSTEM CALLED **FLOWER WAR** (AS OPPOSED TO, Y'KNOW, **WAR** WAR) WHICH WAS LIKE A SORT OF MASSIVE **DUEL**: BOTH SIDES AGREED TO SHOW UP WITH THE EXACT SAME NUMBER OF GUYS AT THE SAME TIME AND PLACE, SO BOTH COULD CAPTURE VICTIMS FOR SACRIFICE.

ONCE THERE, FOUR PRIESTS HELD THE VICTIM DOWN OVER A LARGE STONE...

NOW THIS IS GOING TO HURT YOU MORE THAN IT HURTS ME...

WHILE A FIFTH CUT OPEN THE CHEST, TORE OUT THE STILL-BEATING HEART AND HELD IT UP AS AN OFFERING TO THE GODS.

THEN THE BODY WAS TOSSED OVER THE EDGE AND DOWN THE STAIRS.

SPLAT!

SPLAT!

THE HEAD WAS CUT OFF AND DISPLAYED ON THE **TZOMPANTLI,** OR WALL OF SKULLS.

WHILE THE GOOD BITS OF THE VICTIM, ESPECIALLY THE HANDS AND LEGS, WERE SERVED UP WITH CORN TORTILLAS TO THE WARRIOR WHO'D CAPTURED THEM.

MAYBE WITH A CUP OF **XOCOLATL,** OR, AS **YOU** CALL IT, **CHOCOLATE!** SO THINK ABOUT **THAT** NEXT TIME YOU'RE ENJOYING A NICE CUP OF COCOA!

WITHOUT A SON, THE **TUDOR DYNASTY** WOULD **DIE OUT!**

I NEEDED A **NEW WIFE**, AND **FAST!**

...AND I ALREADY HAD SOMEONE IN MIND FOR THE JOB...

ANNE BOLEYN! PRETTY, CLEVER, CHARMING; SHE HAD ME IN A WHIRL!

BUT THE CHURCH DIDN'T ALLOW **DIVORCE.** YOU APPLIED TO THE POPE FOR **SPECIAL PERMISSION.**

BUT HE WOULDN'T ALLOW IT!

BUT THEN I GOT THINKING... WHY SHOULD THE KING BE TOLD WHAT TO DO BY **ANYONE!?** WASN'T I APPOINTED BY **GOD!?**

WHAT IF I MADE MY **OWN** CHURCH? THEN **I'D** BE IN CHARGE AND I COULD DO WHAT I LIKED!

SO THAT'S JUST WHAT I DID! I GAVE MY WIFE THE BOOT AND MARRIED ANNE INSTEAD.

THE POPE **EXCOMMUNICATED** ME, BUT I DIDN'T CARE. I HAD MY **OWN** CHURCH NOW.

AND THE FUN DIDN'T STOP THERE! I ALSO GOT RID OF ALL THE MONASTERIES AND KICKED OUT THE MONKS.

I **NEEDED** THAT LAND TO BRIBE - I MEAN **REWARD** MY LOYAL SUPPORTERS.

YOU KICKED OUT THE MONKS!? PEOPLE WHO DEVOTED THEIR LIVES TO HELPING OTHERS!?

PFF. PARASITES!

OK, SOME PEOPLE GOT MAD.

THEY HAD A BIG REBELLION IN THE NORTH, BUT I FIXED 'EM! I TOLD THEM TO COME TO LONDON FOR PEACE TALKS...

...AND THEN EXECUTED THEM ALL FOR TREASON!

SO, SINCE YOU'RE THE KING, YOU DON'T HAVE TO KEEP YOUR PROMISES?

RIGHT! EXACTLY! I KNEW YOU'D GET IT!

AND YOU DIDN'T KEEP YOUR PROMISES TO ANNE, EITHER...

SHE DIDN'T KEEP HER PROMISES TO ME!

SHE WAS SUPPOSED TO GIVE ME A SON! BUT ALL I GOT WAS ANOTHER DAUGHTER...

FAT LOT OF GOOD THAT DID ME!

SPEAKING OF FAT... I NOTICE YOU STARTED PUTTING ON A LOT OF WEIGHT ABOUT THIS TIME...

HEY! I'M NOT FAT! I'M HUSKY. IMPOSING. POWERFULLY BUILT.

YOU NEEDED A TEAM OF SERVANTS JUST TO GET YOU UP THE STAIRS...

OK, I GOT A BIT BIG TOWARDS THE END...

I HAD A JOUSTING ACCIDENT THAT MEANT I COULDN'T DO ANY MORE EXERCISE, SO IT PROBABLY CAME FROM THAT.

OOPS! SORRY... NO HARD FEELINGS, EH? YOUR MAJESTY...?

AND THE ENORMOUS BANQUETS.

OK, AND THE ENORMOUS — WHY ARE WE STILL TALKING ABOUT MY WEIGHT? YOU'RE ONLY ON WIFE NUMBER TWO!

WIFE NUMBER **ONE**: **CATHERINE OF ARAGON**. YOU WERE BROUGHT OVER FROM SPAIN, AGED JUST **16**, TO MARRY HENRY'S OLDER BROTHER, **ARTHUR**.

YES. HE DIED. SWEATING SICKNESS. VERY SAD. WE WERE MARRIED FOR JUST A FEW MONTHS.

CORPSE TALK "I MARRIED MY DEAD HUSBAND'S BROTHER."

HENRY'S DAD WANTED TO PRESERVE THE ALLIANCE WITH SPAIN, SO HE ARRANGED FOR ME TO MARRY HENRY WHEN HE GREW UP.

SO YOU DIDN'T MARRY HENRY FOR LOVE?

DON'T BE **SILLY**! KINGS AND QUEENS CAN'T DO THAT — THERE'S TOO MUCH AT STAKE!

SPEAK FOR YOURSELF!

HUH? WELL, IT DIDN'T WORK OUT WELL FOR **YOU**, DID IT!?

OH YEAH!?

LADIES! LADIES!

WE'LL GET TO THAT... NOW, YOU WERE HAPPILY MARRIED FOR **15** YEARS. WHEN DID THE TROUBLE START?

HENRY WAS OBSESSED WITH HAVING A **SON**, SO HE COULD CONTINUE THE **DYNASTY**.

AND YOU DIDN'T GIVE HIM ONE.

I GAVE HIM **MANY** SONS! BUT THEY ALL **DIED**. IT WAS THE MIDDLE AGES — PEOPLE DIED ALL THE TIME!

SO HENRY MOVED ON TO **ANNE BOLEYN**! YOUNG, GLAMOROUS AND NEWLY RETURNED FROM FRANCE...

ANNE, LET'S GO TO YOU NOW. YOU ENSNARED THE KING WITH YOUR BEAUTY AND SPARKLING PERSONALITY. BUT YOU COULDN'T GET MARRIED.

IT'S ALL **HER** FAULT, THE COW!

CORPSE TALK "I STOLE A HUSBAND, BUT THEN HE KILLED ME!"

HE WAS MINE! YOU STOLE HIM!

HOME WRECKER!

WITCH!

HE DESERVED BETTER!

OLD HAG!

POO HEAD!

ALL RIGHT. LET'S KEEP THIS **CIVILISED**, SHALL WE?

ANNE, WHY ON EARTH ARE **YOU** MAD WITH CATHERINE? AFTER ALL, **YOU'RE** THE ONE WHO STOLE **HER** HUSBAND!

SHE COULD'VE JUST GIVEN HIM A DIVORCE. SHE WAS TOO OLD TO HAVE MORE KIDS ANYWAY! BUT SHE HAD TO BE ALL "OOH, HE'S MY HUSBAND"!

HENRY **LOVED** ME! HE WROTE ME LOVE LETTERS ALL THE TIME! AND HE **HATED** WRITING!

THAT'S TRUE.

HE DID HATE WRITING.

WHO WOULDN'T?

BUT ALL HIS LOVE TURNED TO **HATE** WHEN YOU GAVE HIM, NOT A MALE HEIR, BUT A **GIRL**!

YEAH, ANNE. SERIOUSLY.

IF YOU'D JUST AGREED TO THE DIVORCE I'D HAVE HAD **TIME** TO PRODUCE AN HEIR!

WITCH!

HOME WRECKER!

HAG!

ETC....

SIGH...

84

AND HENRY MIGHT ALSO HAVE BEEN GROWING TIRED OF YOUR INCREASINGLY VIOLENT TEMPER...

VIOLENT!? WHO SAYS I'M VIOLENT? I'LL KICK THEIR PANTS!

BUT HE'D JUST TURNED THE COUNTRY, AND THE CHURCH, UPSIDE-DOWN TO MARRY YOU! HE COULDN'T JUST SAY HE'D CHANGED HIS MIND!

NO. SNIFF. SO HE MADE UP ALL THESE HORRIBLE STORIES ABOUT ME...

THAT I WAS A WITCH, AND THAT I'D FORCED HIM TO MARRY ME WITH MAGIC SPELLS, AND I WAS HAVING AFFAIRS WITH 5 MEN, INCLUDING MY OWN BROTHER!

THERE, THERE DEAR. WE ALL KNEW THEY WERE LIES...

GROSS LIES.

OO HOO HOO!

BUT YOU DIDN'T SAY ANYTHING?

NO ONE SAID ANYTHING!

HE WAS THE KING...

SO ANNE GOT THE CHOP...

AND IN CAME WIFE NUMBER 3...

...JANE SEYMOUR!

"I'D MUCH RATHER BE SEWING."

HUH? WHAT'S THAT?

OH, SORRY. IS IT MY TURN? I'M JUST ON A TRICKY BIT HERE...

JANE, YOU WERE MARRYING A MAN WHO HAD JUST KILLED HIS WIFE! WEREN'T YOU AFRAID?

IN ALL HONESTY, I WAS TERRIFIED!

85

BUT I COULDN'T SAY NO, COULD I? ANYWAY, AS LONG AS I COULD POP OUT A **BOY**, I'D BE FINE...

WHICH YOU DID! AT LAST, THE SON HE'D BEEN LONGING FOR!

PHEW!

GREAT!

OH GEEZ! WHAT?

EXCEPT I DIED TWO WEEKS LATER...

IT WAS THE MIDDLE AGES. PEOPLE DIED ALL THE TIME!

POST-PARTUM INFECTION. VERY COMMON. BUT HENRY HAD ME BURIED IN HIS ROYAL TOMB. AND HE CALLED ME HIS **ONLY TRUE WIFE.**

GRR...

WHICH LEADS US TO WIFE NUMBER **4**, THE GERMAN PRINCESS **ANNE OF CLEVES.**

JA, HALLO!

ANNE, YOU HAD NEVER EVEN **MET** HENRY WHEN YOU ARRIVED IN ENGLAND TO BECOME HIS NEW QUEEN...

JA, IT WAS ANOTHER OF THOSE POLITICAL MARRIAGES. HE WANTED AN ALLIANCE WITH MY FATHER.

CORPSE TALK

"I WAS DUMPED FOR LOOKING LIKE A HORSE!"

HE COULDN'T VISIT SO HE SENT HIS PORTAIT PAINTER TO PAINT MY PICTURE.

PHWOAR! SHE'S A HOTTIE!

BUT, WHEN YOU ARRIVED, YOU DIDN'T MEET HIS EXPECTATIONS?

WELL, THAT'S NOT QUITE THE WHOLE STORY...

APPARENTLY, HENRY HAD AN OBSESSION WITH DRESSING-UP AND PLAYING TRICKS ON PEOPLE. SO HE GOT IT IN HIS HEAD TO "SURPRISE ME"...

HEE HEE! THIS'LL BE GREAT! PLUS, I CAN SEE WHAT SHE **REALLY** THINKS OF ME, NOT AS A KING, BUT AS A **MAN!**

UH...

HENRY STILL THOUGHT HE WAS **HOT STUFF**, BUT THE YEARS HAD NOT BEEN **KIND**...

SO WHEN THIS UGLY, FAT **SERVANT** BURST INTO MY ROOM UNANNOUNCED, HOW WAS I TO KNOW!?

DO YOU **MIND?** I'M **TRYING** TO LOOK OUT THIS WINDOW.

OOPS!

OOPS IS RIGHT! BUT AFTER THAT WE STILL HAD TO GET MARRIED!

AWKWARD!

THANK **GOODNESS** HE SUGGESTED A DIVORCE! I AGREED RIGHT AWAY!

HENRY WAS SO RELIEVED, HE MADE ME THE "**KING'S HONOURABLE SISTER**", SO I GOT TO LIVE IN LOVELY CASTLES AND WEAR FINE JEWELS AND CLOTHES.

RESULT!

I KNOW! PRETTY SWEET!

WELL, AT LEAST **SOMEBODY** GOT A HAPPY ENDING!

...WHICH IS MORE THAN CAN BE SAID FOR WIFE NUMBER **5. KATHERINE HOWARD**, HOW DID **YOU** FEEL ABOUT MARRYING THE OLD, FAT KING?

WELL, OK, LIKE, AT FIRST, I LIKED ALL THE JEWELLERY AND THE, LIKE, ATTENTION...

CORPSE TALK

"DON'T HATE ME COS I'M PRETTY!"

87

OMG! I WAS JUST, LIKE, TOTALLY **POOR** BEFORE!

BUT MY UNCLE WAS, LIKE, TOTALLY THE DUKE OF NORFOLK. HE ARRANGED FOR ME TO COME TO COURT AND LIKE, TOTALLY MEET THE KING.

AND SO, IF **YOU** MARRIED THE KING, YOUR UNCLE WOULD ALSO BECOME MORE POWERFUL.

...

OMG! THAT'S TOTALLY IT!

THAT EXPLAINS WHY HE WAS ALL LIKE "BE NICE TO THE KING" AND "ACT LIKE YOU THINK HE'S GREAT" AND "DON'T MENTION HIS BIG BELLY".

SO THE KING THOUGHT YOU WERE WONDERFUL. YOU MADE HIM FEEL YOUNG AND LOVED AGAIN.

OK, WELL... HERE'S, LIKE, THE THING. BEFORE, I LIVED AT MY AUNT'S HOUSE. SHE WAS TOTALLY OLD AND LIKE, TOTALLY DEAF.

I USED TO LIKE, TOTALLY SNEAK BOYFRIENDS IN THERE ALL THE TIME...

UH-OH! THIS DOESN'T SOUND GOOD.

WELL, THERE WAS LIKE, THIS **GUY**...

THOMAS CULPEPPER! HE WAS ONE OF THE MEN AT COURT. HE JUST LOOKED SO **CUTE** IN HIS TIGHTS AND THOSE POOFY LITTLE LEG THINGS...

SO YOU STARTED HAVING AN AFFAIR.

...

AND THE KING FOUND OUT.

...

I WAS LIKE, TOTALLY IN THE MIDDLE OF A DANCING LESSON WHEN THEY ARRESTED ME.

STEPPIN' OUT ON THE KING, THAT'S **HIGH TREASON**! PLUS, LOOK AT WHAT HAPPENED TO THE **OTHERS**! WHAT **WERE** YOU **THINKING**!

HENRY WAS HEARTBROKEN! (AFTER HAVING YOUR HEAD CUT OFF.) BUT, AMAZINGLY, IT STILL DIDN'T PUT HIM OFF GETTING MARRIED! HE DECIDED **YOU** WOULD BE HIS NEXT BRIDE, CATHERINE PARR...

I DIDN'T HAVE MUCH CHOICE IN THE MATTER. I'D ALREADY HAD **TWO** POLITICAL MARRIAGES, AND WAS LOOKING FORWARD TO MARRYING MY TRUE LOVE, BUT I COULDN'T REFUSE THE KING.

CORPSE TALK

"I KEPT MY HEAD, AND MADE SMALL TALK INSTEAD."

BY THIS POINT, HE WAS TERRIBLY FAT, AND HE HAD AN AWFUL LEG WOUND THAT WOULDN'T HEAL. I KEPT HIM ENTERTAINED WITH DEBATES.

BORING!

HEY! AT LEAST I **SURVIVED**!

OH, RIGHT! BY, LIKE, TOTALLY DISCUSSING **POLITICS**! WISH **I'D** THOUGHT OF THAT!

WELL, MAYBE IF YOU WEREN'T SO **DUMB**, YOU WOULD HAVE!

OH, YOU DID **NOT** JUST SAY THAT! IT IS **ON**!

AND NOW IT'S TIME TO PUMP UP THE VOLUME, CLEAR THE DANCE FLOOR AND GET READY TO **PARTY HEARTY** WITH THE KING WHO BROUGHT THE **GOOD TIMES** BACK TO **GREAT BRITAIN**...

IT'S THE **MERRIE MONARCH** HIMSELF...

CHARLES II!

CHARLES II
ENGLISH KING
1630–1685

ALTHOUGH... YOU'RE PROBABLY BEST KNOWN TODAY AS THE NAMESAKE OF THE **KING CHARLES SPANIEL**!

WHAT!?

WELL LOOK, YOU **DO** HAVE THE SAME HAIRSTYLES...

YOU MUST ADMIT, IT'S PRETTY UNCANNY.

HOW **HUMILIATING**!

HEY, THAT'S HISTORY FOR YOU — ONE MINUTE YOU'RE A BIG SHOT AND THE NEXT, THEY'RE NAMING DOGS AFTER YOU.

RUFF!

BUT LET'S TALK ABOUT YOUR LIFE, COS IT IS PRETTY INTERESTING.

OH, NICE. THANKS **VERY** MUCH.

YOUR FATHER WAS CHARLES I, WHO HAD HIS HEAD CHOPPED OFF BY CROMWELL.

THAT SCOUNDREL!

YOU TRIED TO AVENGE HIS DEATH AND RECOVER YOUR THRONE, BUT YOUR ARMY WAS NO MATCH FOR CROMWELL'S CRACK TROOPS.

CHAAA....

...rge?

I ESCAPED THE BATTLE, BUT I WAS ALONE AND HUNTED, IN THE MIDDLE OF ENEMY TERRITORY, AND SURROUNDED BY PEOPLE WHO HATED MY **GUTS**!

I TOOK REFUGE IN THE COUNTRYSIDE. I ONCE SPENT A WHOLE DAY HIDING UP AN OAK TREE WHILE SOLDIERS SEARCHED FOR ME UNDERNEATH.

IF I COULD GET OUT OF ENGLAND I'D BE SAFE, BUT HOW **COULD** I, WITH CROMWELL AND HIS CREEPS SCOURING THE COUNTRYSIDE...?

I NEEDED A DISGUISE! THE FIRST THING WAS TO CUT OFF MY TRADEMARK HAIRDO.

BUT I COULDN'T DISGUISE MY HEIGHT.

AVERAGE HEIGHT AT THE TIME

HMM...

THAT KING, EH? WHAT A JERK! I HOPE THEY HANG 'IM!

HA HA! YEAH! YOU'RE ALL RIGHT, BIG GUY...

BUT YOU COULDN'T DO IT ALL ALONE!

RIGHT. I NEEDED HELP! AND IT CAME FROM AN UNEXPECTED SOURCE...

THE CATHOLICS! CROMWELL HAD BEEN PERSECUTING THEM FOR YEARS, SO THEY HATED HIM EVEN MORE THAN I DID!

AND OVER THE YEARS OF PERSECUTION, THEY'D DEVELOPED A NETWORK OF SECRET PASSAGES, SAFE HOUSES AND PASSWORDS. VERY USEFUL!

FOR SIX WEEKS I ROAMED ENGLAND, RELYING ON THE HELP OF GOOD PEOPLE WHO KNEW THEY'D BE PUT TO DEATH IF THEY WERE CAUGHT.

EVENTUALLY, I ESCAPED TO FRANCE WHERE I LIVED IN EXILE. I HAD GIVEN UP ALL HOPE OF EVER BECOMING KING. BUT THEN... CROMWELL DIED!

BY THAT POINT, EVERYONE WAS PRETTY SICK OF CROMWELL AND ALL HIS RULES.

NO FUN ALLOWED.

SO I WAS INVITED BACK AND RESTORED TO THE THRONE! IT WAS TIME TO **PAR-TAY!**

YOU BROUGHT BACK ALL SORTS OF FUN STUFF THAT CROMWELL BANNED. LIKE THEATRE, MAKE-UP AND CHRISTMAS! **AND** YOU INTRODUCED THE FRENCH DRINK, **CHAMPAGNE!**

BUT WHAT YOU LIKED **MOST** WAS HAVING LOTS OF **GIRLFRIENDS...**

WHAT CAN I SAY? LADIES LOVE A MAN IN A **CROWN...**

I HAD **LOADS** OF THEM, AND I SHOWERED THEM WITH MONEY, TITLES AND JEWELS!

THE COMPETITION TO BE MY FAVOURITE WAS **INTENSE!** ACTRESS **NELL GWYN** SAW I WAS GETTING FRIENDLY WITH ONE OF HER RIVALS.

SO SHE CAME UP WITH A **CUNNING PLAN**. WHENEVER WE HAD A DATE, NELL LACED THE POOR GIRL'S CAKE WITH A POWERFUL **LAXATIVE**...

IT MADE HER SPEND THE WHOLE NIGHT **POOPING**!

ARE YOU OK IN THERE...?

OOH!

A **JOB** WELL DONE!

WHAT A **PARTY-POOPER**! BUT IT WASN'T ALL FUN AND GAMES. THE DIFFERENT RELIGIOUS GROUPS WERE STILL KNOCKING **LUMPS** OUT OF EACH OTHER.

RIGHT. THE CATHOLICS GOT A PARTICULARLY HARD TIME OF IT. **EVERYBODY** HATED THEM!

A GUY CALLED **TITUS OATES** CLAIMED TO HAVE UNCOVERED A MASSIVE CATHOLIC PLOT TO KILL ME.

I WAS PRETTY SURE OATES WAS TELLING PORKY PIES — AFTER ALL IT WAS THE CATHOLICS WHO HAD **SAVED** ME FROM CROMWELL!

BUT THE PEOPLE HATED THEM SO MUCH, THEY **BELIEVED** OATES' LIES AND MANY CATHOLICS GOT PUT TO DEATH.

EVENTUALLY, IT CAME OUT THAT OATES WAS A **PROFESSIONAL LIAR**. HE'D MADE THE WHOLE THING UP.

OOPS! SORREEE...

SO WE CAN SEE THAT YOU WEREN'T **JUST** THE PARTY KING, BUT A SERIOUS AND DEDICATED MONARCH WHO...

I JUST **LOVE** WHAT YOU'VE DONE WITH YOUR HAIR...

SPANIEL-STYLED SOVEREIGN **CHARLES II** WAS JUST ONE IN A LONG LINE OF BRITISH KINGS WHO HAD AN -ER- **COMPLICATED** RELATIONSHIP WITH THEIR PARLIAMENTS...

-SIGH- TELL ME ABOUT IT!

I HAD TO BE ALL, "WOULD YOU PLEASE APPROVE MY NEW LAW?" AND, "DO YOU MIND IF I START A WAR?"

NOT LIKE THE GOOD OLD DAYS WHEN A KING COULD DO WHAT HE LIKED...

DON'T YOU MEAN THE **BAD** OLD DAYS...?

WELL, I GUESS THAT DEPENDS ON IF YOU'RE A KING OR NOT.

A KING LIKE **WILLIAM THE CONQUERER** COULD TELL EVERYONE WHAT TO DO BECAUSE HE'D ALREADY BEATEN THEM UP, AND EVERYONE KNEW HE COULD DO IT AGAIN.

MY BARONS WERE MOSTLY FELLOW NORMAN INVADERS, SO THEY FOLLOWED ME BECAUSE I MADE THEM **RICH**!

I WAS STILL **EXPECTED** TO LISTEN TO THEIR ADVICE.

AND I GENERALLY TRIED TO KEEP THEM HAPPY. BUT THERE WAS NO LAW SAYING I **HAD** TO.

LET'S RAISE TAXES!

LET'S START A WAR!

LET'S GET LUNCH!

BAD KING JOHN WAS THE FIRST KING TO BE **FORCED** TO DO WHAT HIS BARONS SAID. HE NEEDED MONEY, AND LOTS OF IT, SO HE DECIDED TO GET A BIT **CREATIVE** WITH HIS NEW TAXES.

YOU WANNA GET MARRIED? SWEET!

THERE'S A TAX FOR THAT.

HOLD ON! **I** DON'T WANNA MARRY THIS BOZO.

OH OK, NO PROBLEM.

THERE'S A TAX FOR THAT TOO.

EVENTUALLY, MY BARONS REBELLED AND **FORCED** ME TO SIGN THE STUPID **MAGNA CARTA** (THE NAME JUST MEANS "BIG CONTRACT"), PROMISING TO FOLLOW THEIR ADVICE.

PFF. LIKE I'M ACTUALLY GONNA **KEEP MY PROMISES.**

JOHN'S SON **HENRY III** CARRIED ON THE FAMILY TRADITION OF CHEESING OFF THE BARONS, THIS TIME BY GIVING ALL THE CUSHY JOBS TO HIS BUDDIES. HE ACTUALLY GOT CAPTURED AND REPLACED FOR A WHILE BY REBEL BARON **SIMON DE MONTFORT**.

THE KING SHOULD RULE FOR THE GOOD OF **ALL**, NOT JUST HIS FAVOURITES!

YOU WERE HAPPY ENOUGH WHEN **YOU** WERE THE ONE GETTING THE FAVOURS...

I WAS ALSO THE FIRST RULER TO INCLUDE **COMMONERS** IN MY PARLIAMENT.

SEE? I'M A MAN OF THE PEOPLE!

NOT AT ALL AN ILLEGAL USURPER DRUNK ON POWER, NO SIRREE!

BY THE TIME OF **HENRY VIII**, IT WAS STANDARD PRACTICE FOR THE KING TO CALL A PARLIAMENT OF BOTH LORDS **AND** COMMONS WHEN HE WANTED TO CHANGE A LAW.

I STUFFED PARLIAMENT WITH MY OWN GUYS, AND THEN THREATENED THEM ALL WITH EXECUTION, SO IT'S NOT LIKE THEY WERE REALLY GOING TO VOTE AGAINST ME...

BUT EVEN WHILE MAKING MYSELF **GOD'S SUPREME AUTHORITY**, I STILL HAD TO AT LEAST MAKE IT **LOOK** LIKE PARLIAMENT AGREED WITH ME.

ALL IN FAVOUR OF HENRY FOR HEAD OF THE CHURCH, MAN OF THE YEAR AND "MOST HANDSOME KING"...?

GREAT IDEA!

AYE!

AYE!

OK, SO, HENRY ALWAYS HAD A BIT OF A EGO PROBLEM.

BUT THIS THING ABOUT MAKING HIM THE HEAD OF THE CHURCH WAS JUST ONE PART OF A MASSIVE RELIGIOUS MOVEMENT SWEEPING EUROPE...

THE **PROTESTANT REFORMATION**.

HENRY'S NEW CHURCH STILL LOOKED A LOT LIKE THE OLD ONE, JUST WITH **HIM** AT THE TOP INSTEAD OF THE POPE.

BUT OTHER, MORE RADICAL CHURCHES ARGUED THAT ALL PEOPLE ARE EQUAL BEFORE GOD.

AND FROM THERE IT WAS A SHORT STEP TO ARGUING THAT PEOPLE SHOULD HAVE AN EQUAL SAY IN HOW THINGS ARE RUN.

THESE TWO IDEAS BECAME MORE AND MORE EXTREME UNTIL THEY CAME TO A HEAD IN THE REIGN OF MY DAD, **CHARLES I**...

I'M APPOINTED BY **GOD!**

YOU ALL HAVE TO DO WHAT I SAY!

CHARLES AND HIS PARLIAMENT ENDED UP FIGHTING THE **ENGLISH CIVIL WAR** OVER WHO GOT THE FINAL SAY IN RUNNING THE COUNTRY.

YOU'RE APPOINTED TO SERVE GOD'S PEOPLE!

YOU HAVE TO DO WHAT **WE** SAY!

BUT EVEN AFTER LOSING, CHARLES I KEPT INSISTING HE COULD DO WHATEVER HE LIKED, SO IN THE END THEY **EXECUTED** HIM.

I'M STILL RIGHT, YOU KNOW...

THE HEAD OF PARLIAMENT'S REBEL ARMY, **OLIVER CROMWELL**, TOOK OVER AND BECAME **ROYAL PROTECTOR**.

NO CROWN.

JUST RAW, NAKED POWER PLEASE.

AND THAT COULD'VE BEEN THAT. NO MORE KINGS, JUST A PURITANICAL, RELIGIOUSLY-INSPIRED **DICTATORSHIP**.

BUT IT DIDN'T TAKE LONG FOR EVERYONE TO GET PRETTY SICK OF PURITANS LIKE CROMWELL, SINCE THEY BASICALLY BANNED EVERYTHING **FUN**.

NO PARTIES

NO THEATRE

NO ENJOYING YOURSELF

SO WHAT **CAN** WE DO?

READ THE BIBLE.

HERE YOU GO.

AND THEN AFTER CROMWELL DIED, HIS SON DIDN'T REALLY WANT THE JOB.

SO THEY ASKED **ME** TO COME BACK!

YAY! CHAMPAGNE AND PARDONS FOR EVERYONE!

AND NOW, MEET THE **SCAPEGOAT SOVEREIGN** OF THE **ANCIEN RÉGIME**, THE ROYAL WHO **WRESTLED THE REVOLUTION** AND LOST!

LET'S HEAR THE RICHES TO RAGS STORY OF THE **LAST QUEEN OF FRANCE**...

MARIE ANTOINETTE!

MARIE ANTOINETTE
FRENCH QUEEN
1755–1793

MARIE, YOU LIVED IN LUXURY WHILE YOUR PEOPLE STARVED. WHEN YOU HEARD THAT THEY COULDN'T AFFORD BREAD, YOU FAMOUSLY SAID "**LET THEM EAT CAKE**"!

THAT'S PRETTY **COLD**!

VILE SLANDER! TOTALLY NOT TRUE!

BUT IT'S ONE OF THE MOST FAMOUS THINGS ABOUT YOU...

UGH! I CAN'T BELIEVE THAT AFTER ALL THIS TIME, PEOPLE ARE **STILL** TELLING **LIES** ABOUT ME!

THE SAME THING HAPPENED AT COURT! THE PEOPLE WERE ALWAYS POLITE TO MY FACE, BUT BEHIND MY BACK THEY SPREAD THE MOST **HORRIBLE GOSSIP** ABOUT ME! THERE WAS NO WAY TO ESCAPE IT!

WELL, I HEARD THAT SHE...

WHISPER WHISPER

PST PST

YOU **DON'T** SAY!

MY HUSBAND, THE KING, WASN'T MUCH HELP. HE WAS MORE INTERESTED IN PLAYING WITH HIS **LOCKS**...

NOT NOW, DEAR...

SOUNDS LIKE A BIT OF A WEIRD HOBBY...

HE WAS A BIT OF A WEIRD GUY.

IT'S NOT LIKE I **WANTED** TO MARRY HIM. AS A DAUGHTER OF THE AUSTRIAN EMPRESS, I HAD TO MARRY WHOEVER WOULD MAKE THE BEST **ALLIANCE** FOR MY FAMILY.

DO IT... FOR AUSTRIA!

THE FRENCH AND THE AUSTRIANS HAD BEEN FIGHTING FOR AGES, SO OUR MARRIAGE WAS SUPPOSED TO USHER IN A NEW ERA OF **PEACE**.

BUT IT WASN'T VERY PEACEFUL FOR ME. I HAD TO LEAVE MY OLD LIFE AND EVERYTHING I KNEW BEHIND TO TRAVEL TO THE FRENCH COURT.

LITERALLY EVERYTHING. NO FRIENDS, NO SERVANTS, NOT EVEN MY DOGS. I EVEN HAD TO LEAVE MY **CLOTHES** BEHIND AT THE BORDER AND CHANGE INTO FRENCH ONES!

SO YOU WERE UTTERLY ALONE, IN A HOSTILE COURT OF IDLE NOBLES WITH NOTHING TO DO BUT SCHEME AND GOSSIP.

AND PEE.

AND... UM?

YUP.

DESPITE AN ABSOLUTE **MOUNTAIN** OF RULES ABOUT POLITE ETIQUETTE, IT WAS CONSIDERED PERFECTLY NORMAL TO **PEE** WHEREVER YOU FELT LIKE IT.

THE SERVANTS WILL CLEAN IT UP!

MAYBE YOU CAN SEE WHY I RETREATED TO MY OWN, SLIGHTLY LESS STINKY **MINI-PALACE**, AND CONCENTRATED ON **ENJOYING** MYSELF...

...LATE NIGHT GAMBLING PARTIES...

MASKED BALLS AT THE PALACE OF VERSAILLES...

UTTERLY AMAZING HAIRSTYLES...

...AND THE MOST **BEAUTIFUL** DRESSES...

YOU SOON GAINED A REPUTATION FOR **EXTRAVAGANT** SPENDING.

HEY, LOOKING **THIS** GOOD DOESN'T COME CHEAP.

BUT, ALL THIS WAS WHILE PEOPLE WERE **STARVING!**

OH, COME ON! I WAS JUST A TEENAGER! I GOT MARRIED AT **FOURTEEN!**

DON'T TELL ME **YOU** NEVER DID ANYTHING STUPID AS A TEENAGER!

AH... OK...

FAIR POINT.

AS I GOT OLDER I **TRIED** TO BE A MORE RESPONSIBLE QUEEN, SAVING MONEY WHERE I COULD SO WE COULD USE IT TO HELP THE POOR.

BUT IT WAS TOO LATE. THE PEOPLE HAD ALREADY MADE THEIR MINDS UP ABOUT ME.

TWO DISASTROUS **NORTH AMERICAN WARS** THAT BANKRUPTED THE STATE.

NOT TO MENTION AN ENTIRE CLASS OF **PARASITIC NOBLES** BLEEDING THE POPULACE DRY.

BUT **OH NO,** LET'S JUST BLAME IT ALL ON THE QUEEN!

SO WHEN THE FRENCH REVOLUTION HAPPENED, YOU WERE IN **REAL** TROUBLE!

ZUT ALORS! TELL ME ABOUT IT!

A MOB OF STARVING PARISIAN WOMEN, BACKED UP BY GOVERNMENT SOLDIERS (THEY WERE **ALSO** STARVING), MARCHED ON VERSAILLES AND STORMED THE PALACE!

I HAD TO FLEE FROM A GANG OF FURIOUS, KNIFE-WIELDING FISH-WIVES. I BARELY ESCAPED WITH MY LIFE!

AFTER THAT, THE REVOLUTIONARIES KEPT US UNDER **HOUSE ARREST** WHILE THEY FIGURED OUT WHAT TO DO WITH US.

ONE GROUP WANTED TO **KEEP** THE KING AS A SORT OF FIGUREHEAD, WITH PARLIAMENT CALLING THE REAL SHOTS. A BIT LIKE THEY'D DONE IN BRITAIN.

IMAGINE, THE KING, TAKING ORDERS FROM A BUNCH OF **COMMONERS**! I WOULDN'T STAND FOR IT!

HE MIGHT BE A WEIRDO, BUT HE WAS A **ROYAL** WEIRDO.

I CONVINCED HIM TO FLEE THE PALACE, SO WE COULD GATHER AN ARMY AND **SMASH** THIS IMPERTINENT RABBLE.

WE DISGUISED OUR WHOLE FAMILY AS **PEASANTS** AND ESCAPED IN THE NIGHT.

WE ALMOST MADE IT TO SAFETY, BUT SOMEONE RECOGNISED THE KING AS THE SAME GUY WHO WAS ON THE **MONEY**.

ALSO OUR HUGE CART FULL OF LUXURY GOODS MIGHT HAVE TIPPED THEM OFF...

WE WERE CAPTURED, TRIED AS "ENEMIES OF THE REVOLUTION" AND SENTENCED TO **MADAME GUILLOTINE.**

AND, WELL, YOU KNOW WHAT HAPPENED NEXT...

BUT THROUGHOUT IT ALL YOU REMAINED VERY CALM. IN FACT YOU COULD SAY YOU **KEPT YOUR HEAD!**

FUNNY, I'M LAUGHING MY **HEAD** OFF.

DECAPITATION STATIONS

TEEN QUEEN **MARIE ANTOINETTE** LOST HER HEAD TO THAT QUINTESSENTIAL SYMBOL OF THE FRENCH REVOLUTION: THE **GUILLOTINE**.

UGH. DON'T REMIND ME.

NAMED AFTER THE REVOLUTIONARY WHO FIRST PROPOSED IT: **DR JOSEPH-IGNACE GUILLOTIN**.

PERSONALLY, I THOUGHT **ANY** FORM OF DEATH PENALTY WAS **BARBARIC**.

BUT, I ARGUED, IF WE **ARE** GOING TO KILL PEOPLE, LET'S AT LEAST MAKE IT AS **HUMANE** AS POSSIBLE.

THE GUILLOTINE WAS **SCIENTIFICALLY DESIGNED** TO BE QUICK, PAINLESS, AND OFFER AN **EQUAL-RIGHTS EXECUTION** TO ALL CITIZENS.

KEY TO ITS CUTTING-EDGE DESIGN IS THE **MOUTON**, A **40**KG STEEL WEIGHT THAT ENSURES THE BLADE FALLS QUICKLY AND CLEANLY.

THE RAZOR-SHARP STEEL **BLADE** DROPS OVER **2** METERS TO REACH SPEEDS OF **40** MPH.

AT THAT SPEED THE GUILLOTINE CAN SLICE THROUGH A NECK IN **0.005** SECONDS!

FAST ENOUGH THAT YOU WON'T FEEL A THING!

THE **LUNETTE** IS MADE OF TWO HALF MOONS THAT SLIDE TOGETHER TO HOLD THE HEAD IN PLACE.

DURING THE FRENCH REVOLUTION, THE GUILLOTINE EXECUTED OVER **15,000** FRENCH CITIZENS.

AT THE HEIGHT OF THE SO-CALLED **REIGN OF TERROR**, **3,000** PEOPLE WERE GUILLOTINED IN **ONE MONTH**.

THE REGULAR EXECUTIONS BECAME SOMETHING OF A **SPECTATOR SPORT**.

SOME WOMEN EVEN BROUGHT THEIR KNITTING.

THE **BASCULE**, (A WOODEN BENCH SUPPORTING THE BODY) STARTS UPRIGHT AND IS THEN FOLDED DOWN INTO PLACE.

GRAND PANIER — BIG BASKET FOR CATCHING THE BODY.

AS OFFICIAL STATE EXECUTIONERS, **CHARLES-HENRI SANSON** AND HIS SONS CONDUCTED ALMOST ALL OF THE EXECUTIONS IN PARIS.

SANSON SENIOR WAS ANOTHER EARLY ADVOCATE OF A MORE SCIENTIFIC METHOD THAN THE OLD SWORD-BASED BEHEADINGS.

THE REVOLUTIONARY COMMITTEE WAS ORDERING **SO MANY** EXECUTIONS, HE WAS HAVING TROUBLE KEEPING UP WITH DEMAND.

COME ON, SANSON! WE HAVEN'T GOT ALL DAY...

DESPITE ITS CLAIMS OF **INSTANT EXECUTION**, PEOPLE QUICKLY BEGAN WONDERING IF THE GUILLOTINE WAS **REALLY** AS "HUMANE" AS ADVERTISED.

WE NOW KNOW IT TAKES AT LEAST **5** SECONDS FOR THE HEAD TO LOSE CONSCIOUSNESS. THAT'S A LONG TIME TO SPEND ROLLING AROUND IN A BASKET.

SOME VICTIMS' HEADS WERE REPORTED TO GRIMACE, OPEN THEIR EYES, OR EVEN RESPOND TO THEIR NAMES.

WHAT A PAIN IN THE NECK!

PIERRE! CAN YOU HEAR ME!?

WHERE'D YOU LEAVE THE TV REMOTE?

LET'S MEET THE **ORIGINAL CAREER WOMAN!** SHE'S A TOUGH LADY WHO MADE IT AS TOP DOG IN A MAN'S WORLD.

DURING HER LIFETIME, SHE WAS THE MOST **POWERFUL** WOMAN ON EARTH! IT'S...

CATHERINE THE GREAT!

CATHERINE THE GREAT

RUSSIAN EMPRESS
1729–1796

CATHERINE, YOU WERE A MERE **PRINCESS** IN A TINY GERMAN STATE, SO WHEN THE CHANCE CAME TO BE **TSARINA OF ALL RUSSIA,** YOU DECIDED THAT **NOTHING** WAS GOING TO STOP YOU GETTING TO THE TOP!

CERTAINLY NOT A LITTLE THING LIKE ONE OF THE WORLD'S **MOST DIFFICULT LANGUAGES!**

I TOOK A CRASH COURSE IN RUSSIAN. I SPENT LATE NIGHTS PACING THE FLOOR, TRYING TO REMEMBER MY LESSONS.

I WORKED SO HARD, I ALMOST **DIED**!

PLEASE.. JUST ONE MORE..

VERB CONJUGATION...

SO REMEMBER, KIDS, TOO MUCH HOMEWORK CAN **KILL**!

TO BE TSARINA, I HAD TO MARRY THE TSAR, PETER III.

I WAS MATURE, INTELLIGENT, REFINED...

HE WAS STUPID, CRASS, CHILDISH... IN SHORT, A **BOY**.

WELL, COME ON! DON'T BOYS MATURE **SLOWER** THAN GIRLS!?

HE WAS **TWENTY-FIVE**...

HE'S SETTING OFF THE **CANNONS** ALL THE TIME! WE CAN'T GET ANY SLEEP!

HE KEEPS POURING **WINE** OVER MY HEAD!

HE'S MAKING FRIENDS WITH OUR WORST ENEMIES BECAUSE HE THINKS THEY HAVE "**COOL UNIFORMS**"!

AWAY ON HOLIDAY...

HE **BEATS** US!

HE PLAYS THE VIOLIN ALL NIGHT!

BADLY!

WE'RE GOING TO GET RID OF HIM, AND WE WANT **YOU** TO TAKE THE JOB...

EXCELLENT...

PETER WAS ARRESTED AND FORCED TO SIGN AN **ABDICATION ORDER**, GIVING **ME** THE THRONE!

WELL, I GUESS IT MAKES A CHANGE FROM **KILLING** SOMEONE TO SNAFFLE A THRONE!

PLEASE. WE'RE NOT **SAVAGES**...

WE KILLED HIM LATER...

AT LAST, YOU WERE ON **TOP OF THE WORLD**!

IT WAS TIME TO START PUSHING YOUR WEIGHT AROUND, **TSARINA-STYLE**!

I'D BEEN READING A LOT ABOUT SOME **MIND-BLOWING** NEW IDEAS, LIKE THAT EVERYONE SHOULD BE EQUAL, OR THAT THE POOR WERE PEOPLE TOO...

SO I THOUGHT, WHY NOT TRY THEM OUT?

YOU GUYS ARE MY LEGAL COMMITTEE. MAKE IT SO!

HAVE YOU **SEEN** THESE NEW LAWS!?

HELPING THE POOR **INDEED**!

WE'LL LOSE ALL OUR **MONEY**!

LET'S JUST **PRETEND** WE'RE WORKING ON THEM! MAYBE SHE'LL GIVE UP...

AND IN THE END, YOU **DID** GIVE UP! SO MUCH FOR "**THE GREAT**"!

HEY! I NEVER **ASKED** TO BE CALLED THAT! AND ANYWAY, I COULD ONLY **STAY** ALL-POWERFUL TSARINA IF I KEPT MY **NOBLES** HAPPY...

AFTER ALL, THEY GOT RID OF **PETER**, THEY COULD GET RID OF **ME**!

SO I DEDICATED MYSELF TO JUST DOING THE BEST JOB I COULD. I EXPANDED RUSSIA'S BORDERS, BUILT NEW CITIES AND TOWNS, AND I ENCOURAGED ARTS AND LITERATURE.

YES, YES, VERY COMMENDABLE. BUT YOU'RE REALLY MOST FAMOUS FOR HAVING LOTS AND LOTS OF BOYFRIENDS!

GENERALS, DUKES AND NOBLES. YOU SHOWERED THEM WITH GIFTS AND TITLES, AND WHEN YOU GOT BORED, TRADED THEM IN FOR A YOUNGER MODEL!

NEXT!

OH, HERE WE GO... THE DOUBLE STANDARD! LOTS OF KINGS HAD WAY MORE GIRLFRIENDS, BUT BECAUSE I'M A WOMAN...

BUT WHY NOT STOP THE GOSSIP BY MARRYING AGAIN?

I WOULD HAVE. I WAS EVEN IN LOVE WITH ONE OR TWO OF THEM...

BUT IF I MARRIED A MERE DUKE OR COUNT, I'D HAVE TO GIVE UP BEING TSARINA!

SO I GUESS YOU COULD SAY YOU WERE MARRIED TO THE JOB!

AND IT WAS THE JOB THAT KILLED YOU! NOT JOB NUMBER ONE, BUT —ER— NUMBER TWO...

YOU DIED WHILE SITTING ON THE TOILET!

GROAN! YOU HAD TO TELL THAT STORY...

TSARS IN THEIR EYES

CATHERINE'S REIGN WAS PLAGUED BY AN UNUSUALLY LARGE NUMBER OF IMPOSTERS — PEOPLE CLAIMING TO BE MEMBERS OF THE ROYAL FAMILY IN A BID TO TAKE THE CROWN.

THESE INCLUDED NO LESS THAN SIXTEEN PEOPLE CLAIMING TO BE HER HUSBAND PETER III — WHICH SHE COULD BE PRETTY SURE WASN'T TRUE, SINCE SHE'D HAD HIM KILLED.

NOW MEET THE **QUAKE-INDUCING CONQUEROR** WHO **REVOLUTIONISED** TRIBAL WARFARE AND CARVED HIS LEGEND ACROSS THE FACE OF HISTORY IN LETTERS OF **BLOOD**.

IT'S THE **SUPERSTAR SOVEREIGN** OF SOUTH AFRICA...

SHAKA ZULU!

SHAKA ZULU
ZULU KING
c. 1787–1828

SHAKA, YOU RAISED THE ZULU FROM A TINY, INSIGNIFICANT TRIBE TO ONE OF THE MOST POWERFUL AND FAMOUS AFRICAN NATIONS OF ALL TIME. BUT YOUR METEORIC RISE TO POWER HAD A ROCKY START...

YEAH, I HAD IT TOUGH. MY DAD WAS CHIEF OF THE ZULUS. NOT THAT **I** EVER BENEFITED FROM IT.

HE'D GOT MY MOTHER PREGNANT BEFORE THEY WERE MARRIED, WHICH WAS A HUGE SCANDAL.

IT WASN'T ME. MAYBE SHE HAS THE ¡SHAKA.

THE iSHAKA WAS AN INTESTINAL PARASITE THAT MADE IT **LOOK** LIKE SOMEONE WAS PREGNANT WHEN THEY WEREN'T. SO WHEN **I** POPPED OUT, THE NAME JUST KIND OF STUCK.

AS YOU CAN IMAGINE, IT'S NOT EASY GROWING UP WITH THE NICKNAME "INTESTINAL PARASITE".

PLUS MY DAD KICKED ME AND MUM OUT OF HIS HOMESTEAD THE FIRST CHANCE HE COULD, SO WE HAD TO WANDER AROUND LIKE BEGGARS.

SO ONE DAY, YOU GOT SICK OF TAKING IT AND DECIDED IT WAS TIME TO START DISHING IT OUT.

YOUR... SPECIAL TALENTS CAUGHT THE EYE OF A POWERFUL NEIGHBOURING CHIEF: **DISINGWAYO.**

KID, YOU GOT A GIFT. HOW'D YOU LIKE TO JOIN MY ARMY?

THAT SOUNDED GREAT! UNTIL I FOUND OUT JOINING THE ARMY DIDN'T ACTUALLY INVOLVE ANY ACTUAL FIGHTING!

THE TRADITIONAL MODE OF BATTLE STARTED WITH JUST SHOUTING INSULTS FOR A WHILE, THEN THROWING SOME SPEARS (WHICH THE OTHER SIDE WOULD JUST DODGE) UNTIL SOMEONE GOT HURT OR BORED OR RAN AWAY.

BUM HEADS!

POO-POO BUMS!

STUPID BUMS WHO SMELL LIKE BUMS!

SO, BASICALLY, AN ELEGANT SOLUTION FOR SETTLING CONFLICTS WITHOUT MASSIVE BLOODSHED.

I KNOW — WHAT A WASTE!

AS SOON AS I GOT A CHANCE, I DITCHED THE WHOLE THROWING SPEARS THING AND JUST RAN AT THE ENEMY AND STABBED THEM TO DEATH.

GOOD LORD!

WHAT'S GOING ON!?

BUT... BUT... THE RULES...

YOUR STABBY SHENANIGANS QUICKLY CAUGHT THE ATTENTION OF CHIEF DISINGWAYO, WHO PUT YOU IN CHARGE OF YOUR VERY OWN REGIMENT.

AT LAST! POWER! SWEET, SWEET POWER!

I TRAINED MY NEW UNDERLINGS WITH 50-MILE-A-DAY BAREFOOT RUNS ACROSS THE BAKING, ROCKY SAVANNAH TO TOUGHEN THEM UP.

ANYONE ON WHO COMPLAINED WAS PUT TO DEATH. ANYONE WHO DROPPED HIS WEAPON WAS PUT TO DEATH. ANYONE WHO LOOKED TIRED WAS...

I GET IT...

WELL, IT WORKED. I FORGED THEM INTO AN UNSTOPPABLE ARMY OF KILLING MACHINES, AFRAID OF ONLY ONE THING IN THE WORLD: ME!

BUT THIS WAS JUST THE **FIRST** STEP IN MY **MASTER PLAN.** WITH MY NEW SUPER-SOLDIERS, I WAS READY FOR PHASE TWO: THE BUFFALO'S HORNS!

THE WHAT NOW?

FIRST, MY CORE OF HARDENED WARRIORS, THE **BUFFALO'S HEAD,** WOULD CHARGE AT FULL SUPER-SOLDIER SPEED DIRECTLY AT THE ENEMY.

RAAAAAAA   RAAAAAAAA

THEN, OUT FROM BEHIND THEM WOULD SPRING THE TWO **BUFFALO'S HORNS,** ENCLOSING THE ENEMY IN AN IMPENETRABLE STOCKADE OF **STABBINGS.**

SOUNDS PRETTY BRUTAL.

BRUTAL, MAYBE, BUT THE GREAT SHAKA COULD ALSO SHOW **MERCY.** I ALWAYS OFFERED MY DEFEATED ENEMIES THE CHANCE TO JOIN THE ZULUS.

LUCKY THEM...

HEY, IT **WAS** LUCKY FOR THEM!

NOT ONLY DID THEY GET TO AVOID A VIOLENT, POINTY DEATH, BUT THEY BECAME PROUD MEMBERS OF THE MIGHTY **ZULU NATION!**

YOU SEE, BEFORE SHAKA, THERE **WAS** NO ZULU NATION, JUST A BUNCH OF LITTLE CHIEFTAINS, RULING OVER LITTLE VILLAGES.

PEOPLE WERE LOYAL TO THEIR VILLAGE AND THEIR FAMILY; WHICH MEANT THEY WERE ALWAYS FIGHTING **OTHER** LITTLE VILLAGES OVER DUMB STUFF LIKE CATTLE OR WOMEN.

BUT **SHAKA** FOUGHT ONLY FOR **POWER**.

RIGHT. THAT'S **MUCH** MORE SENSIBLE.

HEY, Y'KNOW WHAT? **YOU** TRY AND BUILD AN EMPIRE FROM NOTHING, **WITH** NOTHING BUT **WILL** AND **RAGE** AND **RAW INTELLIGENCE! THEN** YOU CAN SIT THERE AND TAKE CHEAP SHOTS AT SHAKA.

OK, LOOK, I'M NOT DOWN-PLAYING YOUR ACHIEVEMENTS. REALLY. IT'S AN AMAZING ACCOMPLISHMENT. BUT IS IT POSSIBLE ALL THAT **ABSOLUTE POWER** STARTED TO GO TO YOUR HEAD?

LIKE, FOR INSTANCE, YOU HAD HUGE NUMBERS OF PEOPLE KILLED FOR "SMELLING LIKE A WITCH".

SNIFF SNIFF

OR, WHEN YOUR BELOVED MOTHER DIED, YOU ORDERED EVERYONE TO STOP **EATING** TO SHOW THEIR GRIEF AND HAD THOUSANDS EXECUTED FOR NOT LOOKING **SAD** ENOUGH.

NOPE. TOO LATE...

OVER A MILLION PEOPLE DIED AS A RESULT OF ALL YOUR WARS AND MASS EXECUTIONS.

HEY, CAN'T MAKE AN OMELETTE WITHOUT BREAKING A FEW EGGS...

WELL, FEAR ISN'T LOYALTY. WHILE YOUR ARMY WAS AWAY, YOUR LIEUTENANTS GANGED UP, STABBED YOU TO DEATH AND DUMPED YOU IN A PIT.

THOSE JERKS. I BET THEY MADE A RIGHT MESS OF THINGS.

WELL, YES, THEY DID IMMEDIATELY START KILLING EACH OTHER, AND THE WHOLE THING FELL APART.

BUT THE EMPIRE YOU HAD BUILT WAS TOO STRONG TO DIE. EVEN TODAY, ZULU IDENTITY REMAINS AN INTENSE SOURCE OF PRIDE FOR MANY SOUTH AFRICANS.

SEE! PEOPLE'LL FORGIVE **ANYTHING** IF YOU CAN GIVE THEM **PRIDE**!

THAT'S... NOT THE MESSAGE I WAS HOPING TO GET ACROSS...

The Battle of iSandlwana

SHAKA **ZULU** IS BACK TO EXPLAIN HOW HIS MILITARY INNOVATIONS ALLOWED THE ZULUS TO TAKE ON THE VASTLY TECHNOLOGICALLY SUPERIOR **BRITISH ARMY** AT **iSANDLWANA.**

HAVING DISCOVERED **DIAMONDS** A FEW YEARS PREVIOUSLY, THE BRITISH WERE TAKING OVER ALL OF SOUTH AFRICA, SO THEY INVADED ZULULAND TO DISARM THE FAMOUSLY AGGRESSIVE ZULU ARMY.

YEAH, RIGHT! I'D LIKE TO SEE THEM TRY!

USING STEALTH AND DECEPTION, THE MASSIVE ZULU ARMY MANAGED TO GET RIGHT UP TO THE BRITISH BEFORE BEING SPOTTED, AT WHICH POINT THEY LAUNCHED THEIR TERRIFYING BATTLE CHARGE.

FOR A WHILE, THE BRITISH MANAGED TO KEEP THE ZULU AT BAY WITH CONSTANT VOLLEYS OF RIFLE FIRE. THOUSANDS OF ZULUS WERE KILLED OR HORRIBLY MAIMED IN AN UNBROKEN HAIL OF LEAD.

BUT THEN, RUNNING OUT OF AMMO, THE BRITISH STARTED TO FALL BACK TO THEIR CAMP.

JUST THEN, **MKHOSANA**, A ZULU OFFICER, STOOD UP INTO THE ONCOMING RIFLE FIRE, SHOUTING THAT THEY WERE JUST "WIND AND HAILSTONES" AND BERATING THE WARRIORS FOR THEIR COWARDICE. HE WAS IMMEDIATELY SHOT IN THE HEAD, BUT HIS COURAGE INSPIRED THE ZULUS, WHO RESUMED THEIR CHARGE.

SO, OK, I WASN'T THERE (HAVING BEEN MURDERED **50** YEARS EARLIER).

BUT I'M PLEASED TO SEE THE TACTICS **I** INVENTED BEING USED TO SUCH GOOD EFFECT.

USING THE "BUFFALO'S HORNS" FORMATION ALLOWED THEM TO SURROUND AND CRUSH THEIR ENEMIES.

I'M ALSO PLEASED TO SEE THEM USING MOUNTAINOUS LANDSCAPE TO HIDE AND AMBUSH THE ENEMY — I TAUGHT THEM THAT!

HEE HEE   SHH!

BUT MOST OF ALL, IT WAS THE FEARLESS WARRIOR MENTALITY **I** DEVELOPED THAT ALLOWED THEM TO CHARGE HEADFIRST INTO A HAIL OF BULLETS.

2,000 BRITISH SOLDIERS

100 MOUNTED POLICE

600 RIFLEMEN

5 FIELD GUNS

800 LIGHTLY ARMED NATIVE AUXILIARIES

300 NATIVE HORSEMEN

THE BRITISH CARRIED MARTINI-HENRY RIFLES; CAPABLE OF FIRING 25 **KILLER SHOTS** PER MINUTE.

VS

24,000 ZULU WARRIORS

6,000 WARRIORS: "THE LEFT HORN"

5,000 RESERVE WARRIORS: "THE LOINS"

4,000 WARRIORS: THE "RIGHT HORN"

9,000 WARRIORS FORMED THE MAIN FORCE "THE BUFFALO'S HEAD"

THE ZULUS CARRIED TRADITIONAL ASSEGAI SPEARS, KNOBKERRIE CLUBS AND COWHIDE SHIELDS.

DESPITE BEING VASTLY OUTNUMBERED, THEIR SUPERIOR MODERN WEAPONS MADE THE BRITISH CONFIDENT OF AN EASY VICTORY. MAYBE A LITTLE **TOO** CONFIDENT...

ON REACHING THEIR CAMP, THE BRITISH WERE **HORRIFIED** TO DISCOVER THE RIGHT HORN OF THE BUFFALO ENCIRCLING THEM FROM BEHIND THE MOUNTAIN OF iSANDLWANA.

REALISING DEFEAT WAS NOW INEVITABLE, THE BRITISH NONETHELESS FOUGHT ON TO THE **LAST MAN**, FIGHTING HAND-TO-HAND WITH BAYONETS AND RIFLE BUTTS WHEN THEIR AMMO RAN OUT.

OVERCONFIDENCE AND BAD LUCK RESULTED IN THE WORST DEFEAT **EVER** INFLICTED ON THE IMPERIAL BRITISH ARMY BY A NATIVE FORCE.

AND NOW, I'M PLEASED TO INTRODUCE BRITAIN'S **LONGEST REIGNING MONARCH** (OR AT LEAST, SHE **WAS** UNTIL **ELIZABETH II** SMASHED HER RECORD).

IT'S THE **ELEGANT EMPRESS OF THE VICTORIAN ERA**, HER MAJESTY...

QUEEN VICTORIA!

QUEEN VICTORIA
BRITISH QUEEN
1819–1901

YOUR MAJESTY, YOU RULED OVER THE **GREATEST EMPIRE** THE WORLD HAS **EVER SEEN.** IT WAS SAID THE SUN **NEVER SET** IN YOUR DOMINIONS...

BUT EVEN BEFORE YOU BECAME QUEEN, **DARK FORCES** WERE ENCIRCLING YOU...

...IN THE SHAPE OF YOUR **OWN MOTHER** AND HER CHIEF OF STAFF, **SIR JOHN CONROY.**

BETWEEN THEM, THEY MADE MY LIFE **MISERABLE**. THEY SAID IT WAS FOR MY OWN GOOD...

BUT REALLY, THEY HOPED TO BECOME THE **POWER BEHIND THE THRONE**.

SO THEY DEVISED A SYSTEM TO TRAIN ME TO BE **COMPLETELY DEPENDENT** ON THEM!

OOH! DASTARDLY!

THEY KEPT ME LOCKED AWAY IN KENSINGTON PALACE. I NEVER SAW MY FAMILY AND I NEVER HAD ANY FRIENDS!

BUT AT THE SAME TIME, I WAS NEVER ALLOWED TO BE ALONE...

DEAR DIARY...

I HAD TO SLEEP IN MY **MOTHER'S** ROOM...

ZZZ ZZZ ZZZ

I EVEN HAD TO BE HELPED UP AND DOWN **STAIRS**!

THANK GOODNESS I'M HERE TO PROTECT YOU!

IN SHORT, I HAD NO PRIVACY AT ALL!

HAVE ANOTHER SHEET, DEAR.

MOTHER!

BUT THEIR PLAN **BACKFIRED**!

TOO RIGHT IT DID! I GREW TO **HATE** THEM, AND THEIR **STUPID RULES**!

SIR JOHN EVEN TRIED TO **FORCE** ME TO MAKE HIM MY PRIVATE SECRETARY.

JUST **SIGN** IT, YOU STUPID GIRL!

NEVER!

I WAS TO BECOME QUEEN WHEN MY UNCLE, THE KING, DIED. IF IT HAPPENED BEFORE I TURNED **18**, MY MOTHER WOULD GET TO RULE IN MY PLACE!

THE KING HATED THEM TOO, SO HE SWORE TO LIVE **LONG ENOUGH** TO **FOIL** THEIR PLANS!

WHICH HE DID, DYING JUST **ONE MONTH** AFTER YOUR EIGHTEENTH BIRTHDAY!

WOO-HOO! I WAS **QUEEN**!

I COULD HAVE **MY OWN ROOM**!

I COULD WALK DOWNSTAIRS **BY MYSELF**!

PLUS, I COULD SACK THAT HORRIBLE MAN **CONROY**.

TOO BAD YOU COULDN'T SACK YOUR **MOTHER**!

AND SHE WAS STILL LIVING WITH ME BECAUSE IT WASN'T **PROPER** FOR A YOUNG LADY TO LIVE ALONE!

BUT THERE WAS **ONE** WAY...

YOU SHOULD GET MARRIED. THEN YOU COULD LIVE WITH YOUR **HUSBAND**...

PRIME MINISTER

NO **WAY**!

YES WAY!

I DIDN'T **WANT** TO GET MARRIED! PLUS, MY RELATIVES IN GERMANY HAD BEEN COACHING MY COUSIN **ALBERT** TO MARRY ME.

GEEZ! **MORE** UNWELCOME FAMILY INTERFERENCE! I HOPE YOU TOLD THEM TO GET LOST!

WELL, I **WOULD** HAVE...

BUT THEN I MET HIM...

OH, **ALBERT**! WHAT A DREAMBOAT!

HE WAS SO **KIND**, SO **INTELLIGENT**, AND HE HAD SUCH **SPLENDID** SIDE-BURNS, I KNEW THAT HE WAS **THE ONE!**

WE WERE GLORIOUSLY, HAPPILY MARRIED, AND FOR **21 WONDERFUL** YEARS WE RULED TOGETHER.

IT WAS A **NEW ERA** OF **UNPRECEDENTED** INDUSTRY AND INNOVATION...

POOR ALBERT. HE TOOK HIS DUTIES SO **VERY** SERIOUSLY. IN THE END, HE WORKED HIMSELF TO **DEATH.**

JUST.. ONE... MORE..

MUSEUM...

YOU SPENT THE REST OF YOUR LIFE IN MOURNING, LIVING IN SECLUSION AND WEARING ONLY BLACK.

OH, MY POOR DARLING ALBERT...

OO HOO HOO HOO...

THERE THERE. IT'S ALL RIGHT. LET IT OUT...

OK, I'VE HEARD OF BEING **SWEPT AWAY** BY ROMANCE, BUT THIS IS **RIDICULOUS!**

GAME OF THRONES

THE WORLD HAS CHANGED A LOT SINCE QUEEN VICTORIA'S TIME.

FROM BEING A CONTINENT **RULED** BY MONARCHS, EUROPE NOW HAS ONLY **7** COUNTRIES LEFT WITH A KING OR QUEEN.

HEH! THEY DON'T CALL ONE THE **GRANDMOTHER OF EUROPE** FOR NOTHING!

AND INCREDIBLY, ALMOST **ALL** OF THEM ARE A DIRECT DESCENDANT OF **QUEEN VICTORIA**!

WWI WAS ONE OF THE MOST DESTRUCTIVE WARS IN HISTORY.

RUSSIA, BRITAIN AND GERMANY WERE ALL FIGHTING EACH OTHER, AND THEY WERE ALL LED BY MEMBERS OF THE **SAME FAMILY**!

GRR!

YOU'RE GOING DOWN, WILHELM!

ALICE GRAND DUCHESS OF HESSE

EDWARD VII

NICOLAS II

ALIX OF HESSE

LAST TSAR AND TSARINA OF RUSSIA

VICTORIA OF HESSE AND BY RHINE

GEORGE V

MAUD QUEEN OF NORWAY

AFTER THAT, LOTS OF COUNTRIES STARTED DECIDING THEY **DIDN'T WANT** KINGS ANYMORE.

(STARTING WITH THE **RUSSIANS**, WHO EXECUTED THEIR ENTIRE ROYAL FAMILY.)

ALICE PRINCESS OF GREECE

GEORGE VI

OLAV V OF NORWAY

SOPHIA QUEEN OF GREECE

PHILIP DUKE OF EDINBURGH

ELIZABETH II

CURRENT QUEEN OF GREAT BRITAIN

HARALD V OF NORWAY

CURRENT KING OF NORWAY

HELENE QUEEN OF ROMANIA

PAUL OF GREECE

PRINCE CHARLES

PRINCE WILLIAM

PRINCE HARRY

MICHAEL I

LAST KING OF ROMANIA

CONSTANTINE II

LAST KING OF GREECE

123

COMING SOON